DIET, CRIME AND DELINQUENCY

ALEXANDER SCHAUSS

Introduction by Michael Lesser, M. D.

Revised 1981

Copyright 1980, Alexander G. Schauss

Published by PARKER HOUSE,
2340 Parker Street, Berkeley, California, 94704

Fourth Printing

Library of Congress Catalogue Card Number 80-80927

ISBN 0-939764-00-8

Author's photo by Glenn Lawrentz
Portion of Hair Analysis form reprinted by permission
of Mineralab, Inc., Hayward, Cal.
Typesetting by Martha's Vineyard Printing Co.
Appendix II reprinted by permission from J. of Orthomolecular
Psychiatry, Vol. 8, Number 4, 1979, pp. 223-224

CONTENTS

To Sharon,

Patience, Devotion and

Understanding

PREFACE

In 1978, over 12, 000,000 arrests were made of children under the age of eighteen for non-traffic crimes. Over one million children were placed in detention centers for some period of time in 1979. It is estimated that at least one-and-a-half million children will be the victims of parental abuse and neglect in 1980. Alcoholism cost the United States in 1978 over 8 billion dollars in lost revenues due to automobile accidents and acts of violence. On any given day in 1980, it is estimated that over one million people will be on probation or parole, while over 300,000 adult offenders await release from U.S. prisons.

Estimates of the cost of maintaining the criminal justice system range from 30 to 50 billion dollars per year. Add to this total the monetary damage caused by criminals and estimates approach 200 billion dollars per year. This amounts to a dollar loss nearly equivalent to the combined budgets of the U. S. Departments of Education and Health and Welfare.

Environmental exposure to the toxic metal lead has mushroomed to over 500 times that experienced by 16th century man. In 1971, the United States had the dubious distinction of becoming the first people on earth to consume processed foods for more than 50 percent of their diet. Over 4,000 additives can now be found in the American food supply, none of which have ever been tested thoroughly for their effects on our central nervous system. We have become a nation of coffee and soda pop drinkers, fast food consumers and refined carbohydrates junkies, without regard to their disasterous consequences, particularly on our children. Less than 35 years ago hyperactive children were a rarity. Try to find someone in North America today who *does not* know a hyperactive child. The incidence of hyperactivity and learning disability is higher in the United States than in any other country in the world!

Could the way we eat contribute to these problems? Since it may, this book was written to answer those who ask, ''where is the evidence?'' *Diet, Crime and Delinquency* is written for informational and educational purposes only. It is not a self-help book. Treating the problems addressed in this book should only be done by trained professionals.

I wrote this book to encourage professionals and lay people to seek solutions to crime by looking at new dimensions to an old problem.

Alexander Schauss

PROGRESS CAN ONLY BE MADE BY

IDEAS WHICH ARE

VERY DIFFERENT FROM THOSE

ACCEPTED AT THE MOMENT

Hans Selye

INTRODUCTION

We have been trying to understand crime since Cain slew Abel. Like many questions for which there is no clear answer, the dispute centers on "Nature versus Nurture." Criminals are a product either of bad genes or bad mothering.

Now, a new idea has surfaced. The criminal doesn't commit a crime because he was "born bad." He doesn't commit a crime because his mother didn't love him. He is bad because he *feels* bad.

This idea is simple and straightforward. It doesn't depend for its explanation on events which occurred many years in the distant past and about which little now can be done. It doesn't say genetics, for which there can be no solution, short of selective destruction of the race.

That people commit crimes because they feel bad is only common sense, since the feeling and the act are closely related in time.

Let's consider some true examples of the most violent crime, murder. One murderer I knew, a young woman, became paranoid probably due to an overactive thyroid gland. In her hyperexcited state she became fearful of her downstairs neighbor and slew her.

Another case, a young man was prescribed the hormone, testosterone, to treat an impotence problem. The testosterone worked so well, that he used several times the recommended dose. The male sex hormone increases aggressivity, and one day while arguing with his woman, he pulled out a gun and "burned her."

These crimes occured because the criminal was feeling bad at the time. Whether or not they were breast fed or properly toilet trained would appear to be inconsequential to their act. Whether or not they had a criminal genetic background seems unimportant. In both of these cases, as in most crimes, it is the events of the present which are paramount in importance. Neither murderer would have committed their crime in a sober state. The fear and rage they experienced secondary to chemical disturbances in the brain, one due to an overactive thyroid, the other from excessive male sex hormone, led to an altered state of consciousness in which they were unable to control their emotions.

Most violent crime is impulsive, spur of the moment, occuring because the criminal temporarily felt bad. This clarifys something which has always puzzled me. It explains why, when I talk to a criminal days after their crime, they usually seem like regular fellows, not much different than you or I; a frightening thought. It means no one is immune. Normal people can be criminals. But this isn't a new idea. Dostoyevsky said it in "Crime and Punishment,"

Victor Hugo implied it in "Les Miserables."

If we are all potential criminals, if under enough stress and in the right circumstances we are all capable of lying, stealing, cheating, rape and even murder, how come most of us don't? What drives a few over the edge, while most are able to control their impulse and think better of it? This is where diet tells, says Alex Schauss, marshalling some powerful arguments and statistics to prove his point.

It seems incredible that what you eat can make you a criminal. But is it? Most everyone accepts that alcohol or drugs can set the stage for crime. We all know of gruesome crimes committed while in a drunken rage or under the influence of mind-bending drugs. What "Diet, Crime and Delinquency" spells out is that ordinary foods or the lack of them can alter our mind, much like alcohol or drugs, unleashing criminal behavior.

How does this happen? Our brain is no different than the rest of our body. Brain cells require proper feeding in order to function correctly. In fact, the brain is the body's most chemically sensitive organ. Starved for the right nutrients, or "gummed up" by toxic pollutants, the brain can and does go haywire. Alex Schauss explains how sugar starvation, vitamin deficiencies, lead pollution and food allergies can convert a normal brain into a criminal mind. Dostoyevsky used the term, "brain fever"; in fact, food allergy can "inflame" the mind, creating the conditions for crime.

Alex Schauss has been working with criminals and delinquents all his adult life. He has experienced first hand the blind alleys and disillusionment of traditional approaches. He has pioneered this fresh approach to the prevention and correction of crime.

Working with heroin addicts in Harlem in 1968, he noticed that those able to kick their diet of fast foods, colas and refined sugar improved, while those stuck in a "junk food" rut continued to use narcotics. At that time, I was in charge of a narcotic addiction rehabilitation program. We found that physical exercise relaxed the addicts and reduced their craving for narcotics. We also observed then that when the men and women were withdrawn from heroin they developed voracious appetites. The combination of wholesome food, adequate in protein, with daily intense physical exercise turned pale skinny junkies into ruddy faced, healthy, happy men and women.

Serving with Youth Services in South Dakota (1975-77), Alex found that the group homes which did a better job at rehabilitation were the homes where the juveniles enjoyed a better diet. In one group home, "Our Home", in Huron, South Dakota, juveniles stayed only an average of three months, compared to a State average of eighteen months. At "Our Home," juveniles had their own garden, with fresh unprocessed vegetables. No refined sugar, coffee or tea was served, but the youths were allowed wholesome nutritious snacks whenever they wished. Exercise was demanded every day, even in the dead of winter.

Alexander Schauss now directs the American Institute For Biosocial Research, 915½ Pacific Ave., Suite 206, Tacoma, Washington, 98402. The Institute conducts research, publishes a Journal and holds training seminars for criminal justice personnel throughout the United States and abroad.

"Nothing is as powerful as an idea whose time has come." In these dark times of ever increasing violence and crime, I believe that "Diet, Crime And Delinquency" presents the new sensible ideas needed to restore safety and sanity to our world.

Michael Lesser, M.D.
April, 1981
Berkeley, California

I

THE DIET, CRIME AND DELINQUENCY LINK

Jerry's Story

Since birth, Jerry's mother says he has been hyperactive and difficult to manage. When Jerry began kindergarten, he was tested and diagnosed as learning disabled. The psychologist's report describes him as a "hyperactive, distractible child who has difficulty following directions." Although of average intelligence he had a severe motor problem with paper and pencil tasks. As the school years progressed, Jerry's study habits declined and his behavior deteriorated until he became known for his distructive actions in class and on the playground. Due to excessive truancy and his violent behavior he became a loner. A fifth grade psychological evaluation stated that Jerry needed "a highly structured individualized program where he could receive immediate feedback and close supervision."

While only nine he was referred to the probation department for a series of crimes that left his probation officer with the impression that Jerry was "manipulative, immature, street-wise, a liar, and a boy who only fears instant punishment." One year after his first referral to probation by police, he continued to be arrested practically every month for more serious offenses such as burglary until he was finally at age eleven, made a ward of the court. Two months later another psychological evaluation of Jerry was even more pessimistic. "Diagnostically, he falls into the group of severe behavior disorders with no sign of psychosis or other severe mental disorder. Interviewing reveals a beguiling, articulate, sophisticated, and bright youngster who has obvious deficits in conscience. He candidly confesses that he feels no guilt. He has obviously not learned that there are people more powerful than himself, and simply escalates his behavior, looking for someone to stop him." The psychologist concluded that he "was not particularly optimistic about his chances for success."

1

Does Jerry sound familiar? Can anything stop his inevitable drift into a life of crime? Will only expensive state institutionalization stop his criminal behavior? Why, after two years, could Jerry not be brought under control?

Crime In America

Each year over 12 million arrests of children are made for alleged delinquent acts other than traffic offenses.[1]. Of this group, over 2,500,000 are formally arrested and referred to the nation's juvenile courts[2]. This total increases each year. It costs over 10 billion dollars a year to handle these juvenile offenders. During 1978, over one million such juveniles spent at least a few days in a detention center or jail. Each day costs the taxpayer $10 to $35. If the child is sent to a state institution, taxpayer's cost rises to between $6,000 and $35,000 per year. If the juvenile does not stop breaking the law, he or she may eventually join an estimated 310,000 other adult offenders in prisons[3] and 250,000 in jails.

In testimony before the U. S. Senate Appropriation's Subcommittee on State, Justice, Commerce and the Judiciary, in March of 1979, the chairman of the National Conference of State Criminal Justice Planning Administrators, Richard C. Wertz, stated:

"Recent public opinion polls clearly indicate that the American people are fed up with the violence and property loss caused in every community in the country by our lawless elements. They are fed up with the inability of our society to prevent or control crime and delinquency and the inability of our police, courts, corrections and juvenile justice agencies to adequately deal with the criminal offender. No other domestic issue--not health care, not the energy problem, not even inflation--is of greater concern to more of our citizens."[4]

How have we reached this sorry state? Have we been misguided in our efforts at preventing crime and delinquency? The answer, based on recent research and reports, is yes. *In recognizing too much the psychological and socio-economic factors of criminal behavior, is it possible that we have ignored the possibility that poor health, underlying metabolic disorders or inadequate nutrition can be significant factors influencing antisocial behavior?*

As stated by Dr. William H. Lyle, Jr., a former chief psychologist for the Federal Bureau of Prisons:

"The court's limited familiarity with these issues is compounded by the fact that psychologists and psychiatrists tend to reject metabolic, in preference to psychodynamic explanations, more out of ignorance of metabolic issues unfortunately, rather than with good awareness of them."[5]

The contributing factors to juvenile delinquency are many. For decades, the problem of juvenile crime has been seen as the product of only social and intrapsychic factors.[6] Families have been seen as the cause of delinquency.[7] Criminologists have largely ignored disturbed biochemical functioning as a possible cause of criminal behavior. It is just such an interest in our biochemical environment, as achieved by a study of diet and delinquency which is needed to redress the balance.

Dietary Approaches To Criminal Behavior

On June 22, 1977, Barbara Reed, Chief Probation Officer, Cuyahoga Falls Municipal Probation Department (Ohio), reported to the U.S. Senate Select Committee on Nutrition and Human Needs on her experience with 318 offenders. Of these, "252 required attention as to their diet and vitamin needs." Mrs. Reed then reported that "we have not had one single person back in court for trouble who has maintained and stayed on the nutritional diet."

Senator Robert Dole (Kansas) questioned Mrs. Reed, "I wonder how many of these success stories are because of diet and how many are because they may have been receiving special attention, someone cared about their rehabilitation?" Mrs. Reed responded, "I have been in this field for 14 years. I was giving people a lot of loving attention before without nearly the results as now. The two work hand in hand... but, I just don't think probationers heard what we were talking about when they were so disconnected with reality that they couldn't remember what had been said. Now they do remember and it makes a big difference." In concluding her Senate testimony, Mrs. Reed said, "Never before has the court had such a tool for working with the many ill people who find themselves in court. We wonder what the results would be if this method of treatment could also be applied to all those sentenced to jail."[8]

Considerable scepticism persists in the correctional system concerning the need to investigate an offender's diet or metabolic functioning and it might seem rather absurd to consider diet as a cause of antisocial behavior. Current thinking favors psychological influences as dominant in the development of personality disorders and neuroses. Yet, there is still no evidence that punishment, deterrence or over 35 other psychological or sociological factors can account for criminal behavior[9]. To effectively confront criminal behavior, I believe criminology needs to be an interdisciplinary behavioral science[10].

3

Jerry's Story Continued

What happened next to our young delinquent Jerry is a good example of such a new interdisciplinary approach. Two probation officers interviewed Jerry with his family. The officers recalled that, since there were three of Jerry's siblings in the room, "the noise level was tremendous." Jerry could not sit still for even three minutes. He had a difficult time following the officers' conversations and would jump from one subject to another. His mother also seemed distracted and tense. Following the interview, the family was given the Nutrition Behavior Inventory (NBI). The NBI is a severity index test of 50 questions assessing health and behavior, the higher the score over 30 the more likely the individual has nutritionally linked factors affecting their health and behavior. (See Appendix I.) The entire family scored high, with Jerry scoring 83, his mother 97, and his step-father 102.

The second interview with the family was at their home. The high NBI scores and a dietary history indicated that, before the family could be relied upon to participate in any rehabilitation program, the family's diet would have to be improved. The mother helped the probation officer assess the family's diet. Meals in Jerry's home consisted of:

Breakfast - Cereals with great quantities of sugar, milk and white bread.

Between Meals - Cola sodas, desserts, sugary snacks.

Dinner - Usually eaten at a national hamburger chain.

The mother also reported that the family would visit a local bakery to load up with pastries for the week, including a cake or two for Sunday's snacks.[11]

Describing herself as hyperactive "all my life," the mother was often depressed and would awaken during the night, unable to sleep, and restlessly move furniture around. She also described her other children as "fidgety" with her youngest boy, aged 3, "just like Jerry."

Educating the family on the effects of refined sugars on behavior, the probation officers urged them to eliminate as much refined sugar from their diet as possible. In place of the simple carbohydrates, such as sugar, jellies, candy, syrup and honey, the family was instructed to use complex carbohydrates, such as fresh fruits, whole grain cereals and breads, nuts and vegetables.

Jerry's Mom replaced sugared cola sodas with diluted natural fruit juices or herb teas. The refined cereal breakfast was replaced by eggs and whole grain toast.

After a month, Jerry's mother reported he was much better. She felt strongly that the diet was largely responsible for the improvement. Not only Jerry, but all his siblings were "doing better than before." Jerry told the probation officers that he liked his new self. For the first time he seemed to understand that he was close to being institutionalized. He assured the probation officers that he would stay on the diet, even at school, because he wanted to remain at home. The probation department's psychiatrist was impressed by the rapid progress Jerry made in only four weeks. After two months, the probation officers' written prognosis for Jerry changed from "hopeless" to "good."

This is, of course, only an isolated case. As one probation officer wrote, "such anecdotal histories are like standing on sand rather than concrete." A few years ago, I made an effort to determine whether nutritional education would indeed reduce rearrest rates of offenders. Though the results indicate that nutrition education of adult offenders does significantly reduce re-arrests[12], corroborating studies are still needed. Fortunately, such studies began in several locations in the United States in 1979.

Riot Fears May Be A Myth

Many correctional administrators are reluctant to implement either dietary changes or nutrition education programs because they fear the reactions of inmates if, for example, less sugar consumption is suggested. This fear stems from prison experiences with food riots so often portrayed in classic convict movies. This fear, however, appears unfounded, as illustrated by the following actual recent prison experiences.

Morris County's Diet-Vitamin Program:

In 1973, a research team from several universities set up an eight week diet-vitamin program in the Morris County Jail Rehabilitation Center in New Jersey. This program, supported by the U.S. Department of Justice, Law Enforcement Assistance Administration[13] included:

1) Diet education aimed at balancing blood sugar levels
2) Vitamin supplements
3) Availability of high protein evening snacks

The results of this eight-week program were:
1) Reduction of inmates' voluntary sugar intake
2) Improvement in morale, mood and self-motivation and,
3) Improvements in previously measured impaired perceptions

As a result of the success of this program, the research team recommended the following:

   1) Implementation of diet changes and diet education in all jails and prisons to treat low blood sugar

   2) Large-scale studies of the efficacy of vitamins in normalizing perception and behavior

Removing Sugar Reduces Disciplinary Problems:

At the United States Naval Correctional Center in Seattle, Washington, the prison administrator, Chief Warrant Officer Gene Baker, took measures beginning in 1978 to curtail the availability of refined carbohydrates. After attending work shops on nutrition and criminal behavior, he received approval from the prison commander, Capt. Ron Miller, and cooperation from his head cook, Petty Officer Uhl, to reduce the intake of white flour and sugar. His brief to the Bureau of Naval Personnel, Law Enforcement and Corrections Division in Washington, D.C., best summarizes his actions:

"...on 1 November 1978, white flour was removed from the confinees diet and replaced with whole wheat. On 3 February 1979, granulated sugar was removed from the confinees diet. This consisted of removal of all pastries, cakes, ice cream, soft drinks and Kool-Aid. The confinees are allowed a teaspoon of sugar in their coffee [or tea] a day and drink milk or water."[14]

By September 4, 1979, the head cook determined that since ordering the restriction on sugar consumption, actual use by each confinee and staff member had been reduced to less than ¾ of an ounce (19 grams) a day.

What have been the results to date of the directive? In a communique to the U.S. Naval headquarters in Washington, D.C., CWO Baker states;

"Since this time, the medical log shows that a definite decrease in the number of confinees at sick call and on medication has occurred, and that disciplinary reports for this year are down 12 percent from the same time frame of last year."[15]

The Purple Heart Homestead:

In Fairmount, Illinois, Tamara Youngman operates a small group home for delinquent and incorrigible juveniles called the Purple Heart Homestead. Juveniles are referred to the Homestead by the Champaign County Probation Department and the Illinois Department of Corrections.

Tamara believes a low sugar diet eliminates the mood swings of her charges, while a vegetarian diet reduces their hostility and aggression. Letters from correctional officials and local press clippings support her statements. One regional correctional administrator told her that they had been consistently pleased with her ability to work "with those youths who have most often been cast out of every known institution from family to school." Along with a structured program of work, psychological counseling, and house rules, the diet and nutrition program is considered essential to the rehabilitation process.

From the day they arrive, all youths are placed on a balanced, natural foods, vegetarian diet. This diet is complete in all essential and nonessential amino acids, vitamins and minerals. The vegetarian diet is ovo-lacto (includes: eggs, milk and cheese), and low in sugar to prevent disturbing highs and lows in the blood sugar. Generally, by six weeks this diet produces a marked drop in aggressive behavior. Dietary measures include drug detoxification, since nearly all of the youths have abused drugs, alcohol or nicotine. Megavitamin therapy is used to correct any chemical imbalance from previous drug abuse. Nutritional and vitamin-mineral deficiencies and imbalances are determined by a physician's examination at a local clinic.

The Chrysalis Program:

Through a grant funded by the National Institute of Alcohol Abuse and Alcoholism, the Chrysalis Outpatient Treatment Program in Minneapolis, Minnesota, has incorporated nutritional counseling into its program. Chrysalis primarily serves women and their children affected by alcohol or drug abuse. The center is unique in that it offers nutrition education and counseling to a large population of Native Americans.

According to Linda Harding, the Child Treatment Program Manager, the program's nutritional counseling has resulted in dramatic improvements in some of the women's ability to cope with drug abuse; improvements not heretofore witnessed in otherwise similar programs.

On glucose tolerance testing (GTT), over 90 percent of the clients are found to be suffering from low blood sugar (hypoglycemia). In almost all cases improvements were clinically documented when the clients eliminated all refined carbohydrates, caffeine, cigarettes, and took large doses of niacin (Vitamin B_3) and Vitamin C.

The Chrysalis nutritional program offers an on-going lecture series presenting tapes of physicians working with this mode of treatment. The program also teaches sugar-free cooking, and sponsors a nutrition support group to help reinforce dietary changes and overcome the difficulties of withdrawal from sugar, nicotine and caffeine.

Is it true, as many correctional officials contend, that eliminating sweets and sodas from the diet would be resisted by confined delinquents or adult inmates? Would most offenders resist taking vitamins or eating an unprocessed diet? To answer these questions, I met with hundreds of delinquents and adult offenders throughout the United States.

Prisoner's Ask for Supplements and Better Diets

In early 1978, I met with 25 hard core adult offenders at a self-help meeting at the U.S. Penitentary, McNeil Island, Washington. Inmates asked me about my work with offenders. When I mentioned that nutrition was one tool in my rehabilitation approach, many more questions were suddenly directed at me. Soon, inmates began to volunteer information about their diets when not in prison. Listening to each other, they laughed. It seemed all of them ate basically the same junk foods. Some became so curious about the role diet might play that they commenced a study evaluating their institution's diet for its effect on their health and behavior. Based on this study, over 40 inmates appealed to the Federal Bureau of Prisons to alter their diet.[16] They requested the elimination of large quantities of refined carbohydrates, increased availability of nutritional supplements, and more whole unprocessed foods.

The following is a portion of one brief filed by a middle aged inmate to the Federal Bureau of Prisons:

''...in analyzing my diet over many years (using hindsight), I find that a diet high in refined carbohydrates and low in many essential nutrients is very probable. I have long been a person who has primarily existed on cola sodas, chocolate products, potato chips, etc., rather than a variety of whole unprocessed fruits, vegetables, nuts and whole grains. The latter are essential to my receiving a balanced diet. Thus, I believe my nutritional deficiencies are of a long duration and may very well be at a critical stage.''

Another inmate's findings:

''...Research I have done into nutrition and my particular metabolic needs seems to indicate that my nutrient needs far exceed U.S. RDA's (Recommended Dietary Allowances). In early 1978, after receiving some vitamins in a Christmas package I noticed an improvement. When the vitamins ran out, I noticed a negative effect on my general metabolism. When I was taking the small amounts of vitamins Dr. [ ] prescribed earlier this year, I could again notice a slight improvement...

In comparing the food tables of the Department of Agriculture with foods available to me, I have determined that some of the essential nutrients, such as several B complex vitamins, are below RDA's, while others are close to the RDA's. But none of the nutrients are at the levels my metabolism indicates are needed for optimum health (the inmate was six and a half feet tall and weighed 260 pounds)... the most important reason why the RDA's are meaningless to optimum health is that they represent the levels of nutrients (vitamins and minerals) required to prevent immediate recognizable deficiencies in the average person. The RDA's do not take into account biochemical individuality, as suggested by Dr. Roger Williams, University of Texas (see Nutrition Against Disease). They do not seriously consider differences in life-style, environment, height, weight, occupation, temperament, emotional stress, illness, metabolic error, bad habits, activity and the like, even though they claim to do so. They consider only the lowest nutrient level required to keep the idealized non-existent 'reference man', who is supposed to be the average healthy person, free from signs of deficiencies."[17]

This same person went on to request:

"I would like to see if vitamin and mineral supplements in megadoses will aid in my metabolism of carbohydrates, lessen my psychological dependency on the many high carbohydrate foods I now crave, and raise my state of health...for future correctional treatment programs, *I am willing to help you on such a project and I am familiar with other problem inmates who would also volunteer for such a study.*"

It seems clear from the above inmate's comments that he would not resist the suggestions made in this book.

The request of these 40 plus inmates was denied by the Bureau of Prisons on the grounds that their diets met all the RDA's! It is as if the Bureau didn't comprehend the reasons for their request. A 6'6" tall and 260 pound man needs more nutrients than the RDA of a 5'7" tall and 145 pound reference man. He does not simply need more carbohydrates.

On November 21, 1979, the Federal Bureau of Prisons did approve the sale of a limited number of nutritional supplements to inmates at their medium security facility in Lompoc, California. Two days after placing the supplements on sale (wheat germ capsules, bone meal tablets, and dessicated liver tablets), the commissary was sold out.

One inmate observed the changes and wrote the following:

"Several of the guys who are taking these supplements, including myself, have noticed a 'wired' or 'high energy' effect, causing a more positive attitude. One fellow commented that it all might be psychological, but after taking the supplements, he hasn't felt so good in longer than he can remember. Whether the "high" is psychological doesn't really matter. Of most importance is the motivating factor that urges one to improve health that comes from feeling good and able to function versus the drugged down feeling that so many suffer. I notice that supplements motivate a feeling of health and hope in me, also in others around me, many of whom have shown little or no sign of hope before. In fact, I saw guys smile today that I had never seen smile before, that really is encouraging."

He continued:

"I can't help wondering, and the guys I come in contact with often ask the question, how is it possible that the BOP [Bureau of Prisons] can deny convicts vitamins? Especially in view of all the damaging, carcinogenic foods that the BOP does sell in the prison commissary (i.e., cigarettes, coffee, sugar, etc.).[18]

Part of the reason the Federal inmates requested improvements in their diets was the self-study program. There are probably many other ways to gain the cooperation of confinees around diet education and dietary improvements.

At the invitation of a large state juvenile institution, I presented a short program on diet and behavior to a meeting of staff and juvenile confinees. Once the role of diet and behavior was brought up, the juveniles asked a number of questions and seemed eager for the information. Later they told the other residents at the facility about the lecture. Many began refusing sweetened foods and drinks and stopped adding sugar to their food. Within two weeks one of the youths who had changed his diet experienced such significant improvement in his behavior, it was noticed by both the staff and other residents.

But subsequently, when a request was made by the same institution to have a larger contingent of residents and staff receive the same lecture, it was rejected by the state offices because too much emphasis was being placed on diet rather than more acceptable and conventional treatment modalities.

However the institution's staff pursued their private study of nutrition and diet outside the institution. As a result, residents of the facility are slowly learning about the importance of nutrition from staff. With few exceptions, inmates are more willing to accept dietary changes than staff.

Dietary Changes In Other Correctional Programs
Oakland, California:

Herb Goldsmith, Food Service Manager for the Alameda County Probation Department, Oakland, California, has responsibility for supervising the preparation of over 1,000 meals a day for over 350 juveniles at two youth camps, a dependent child care facility, and the county juvenile detention center. In early 1979, Mr. Goldsmith decided to slowly reduce the consumption of granulated sugar and sweetened foods by juveniles in his dining rooms. Cereals excessively sweetened by sugar were the first to be removed. Sweetened canned fruits were replaced by fresh fruits. Sugar dispensers were eliminated from dining hall tables and replaced by pre-measured granulated sugar packets. Ice cream and many other high sugar foods were similarly eliminated. Within five months he was providing the juveniles a much healthier and more balanced diet. Additionally, he discovered he was now saving money on food![19] Although some of the staff resisted these changes, Chief Probation Officer Robert Shaner, Director of Special Services, Ray L'Esperance, and Flo Slater, department training officer, provided strong support. Mr. L'Esperance has reported to me that since the changes have been instituted the detained juveniles are "quieter and less rambunctuous."[20] The Alameda County Probation Department's administrative support, in-service training of staff, and staff self-study approach provide a successful model of how institutional dietary changes can be implemented.

San Luis Obispo's Clinical Ecology Program:

In 1979, the San Luis Obispo Juvenile Probation Deprtment in California was awarded a 12-month grant to set up a Clinical Ecology Treatment Program to work with difficult juvenile offenders. A thorough biochemical and nutritional analysis was conducted on each child. No potentially successful rehabilitation tool was abandoned in an effort to provide a total treatment approach. However, biochemical imbalances and nutritional habits were given considerable attention in all cases.

11

According to Wendy Weir, program nutrition consultant, all of the first 15 juveniles handled by the program had significant body chemistry imbalances. The children were subject to environmental and food allergies which were negatively affecting their physiological and psychological processes. "These problems were approached through dietary change", stated former program director, Ken Schmidt.

Besides family nutrition education classes, visits were made to each child's home in order to individually identify and eliminate dietary allergens (i.e., food chemical additives and specific foods) and environmental chemical hazards (i.e., detergents, cleaning agents, sprays, inhalants, perfumes, etc.). Family members were taught how to read and interpret package labels. A trip was also made with the family to their grocery store to teach them how to identify safer and more nutritious foods. If requested, recipes and cooking instructions were provided.

The program interwove nutrition education sessions and Parent and Youth Effectiveness Training (PET/YET) by utlizing a licensed PET/YET instructor and the nutrition consultant. In his report to the Law Enforcement Assistance Administration, U.S. Department of Justice, Ken Schmidt states, "This family approach promises to be very successful in providing improved communication and problem-solving skills which can then be applied to the difficult task of making significant nutritional/dietary changes in the family." He further notes, "in this type of supportive family environment, teenagers are much more likely to be able to make the long-term dietary changes necessary to act as a foundation for the establishment of more acceptable behavioral patterns."[21]

Of the first 20 juveniles in the program given a glucose tolerance test (GTT) for possible blood sugar imbalances, 16 were clinically shown to be hypoglycemic and one was pre-diabetic. One boy refused to be tested but exhibited all the symptoms associated with low blood sugar, while one girl was not given the GTT because she had a seizure disorder.

A typical case was one 14-year-old boy referred to the San Luis Obispo program after being expelled from school for among other things attacking a school official. His behavior fluctuated; usually violent and disobedient, but sometimes well enough to be awarded "school student of the month." He was bright but nonverbal.

Because of frequent petit mal seizures, he was considered "strange" by classmates. Medication controlled his grand mal seizures, but his petit mal continued in the form of sleepiness, "spaced-out" feelings, and occasional black-outs. He reported several stress-related seizures at school. When these occured, he became violent. Testing revealed a markedly elevated aluminum level, which some researchers report is related to certain seizure disorders. The program worked with the youth to eliminate all sources of aluminum, (soft-weave aluminum cookware, deodorants, soda cans, etc.).

His diet also revealed a high consumption of milk (48 to 56 ounces per day) and milk allergy was suspected. After removing him from all dairy products for two weeks, he was seizure-free for a week. At that time he consumed a half gallon of milk and had four seizures that afternoon. This sequence was repeated several times with the same results until he became convinced that milk triggered his seizures and he stopped all dairy products. This reduced the frequency of his seizures to one every two or three weeks.

Another case, a fifteen year old delinquent girl entered the program after a year's hospitalization for extremely violent behavior and seizures, requiring continual medication. Under the careful supervision of a physician, she was placed on the program's corrective diet. Rarely before in her troubled life had she eaten fresh fruits and vegetables. Over several weeks, her violence and seizures subsided until she was able to function completely without medication.

The teenagers participating in the Clinical Ecology Treatment Program had a very high incidence of medical problems during their childhood, supporting the notion that a "bad" child is often a "sick" child.

Excessive Milk Consumption

In 1978, Dr. Clifford E. Simonsen, criminologist at the University of Washington, and I completed a study of the dietary habits of chronic juvenile offenders. Assited by Dr. Jeffrey Bland, biochemist at the University of Puget Sound in Tacoma, the dietary intake of 30 chronic juvenile offenders was evaluated and compared to that of a group of behaviorally disordered children from the local school district. The moderate to severly behaviorally disordered children were the same age as the delinquents, lived in the same geographical area and had similar socio-economic profiles.

Would their diets reveal any significant differences? Might such a study provide a clue as to why one group of youths was constantly in trouble with the law and not the other, even though the non-offenders had chronic behavior problems? (See nutritional data for both groups in Appendix II.)

After analysis of the data, the one factor found to be statistically different between the two groups, was their milk consumption (the p value for the data was .0001)[22] The male offenders consumed an average of 64 ounces of milk a day, while their comparison group only drank an average of 30 ounces daily. Similarly, the delinquent females drank an average of 35 ounces of milk a day, while the comparison group of non-delinquent girls consumed only 17 ounces daily. Among the delinquent boys, two reported drinking more than 113 ounces of milk or over 14 eight ounce glasses a day.[23] In all cases, the milk consumed was of the processed homogenized/pasteurized type. It's possible that the milk processing itself may be a significant factor. We have not yet analyzed whether unfortified pasteurized/homogenized milk, certified raw milk, powdered milk, or goat's milk would similarly be consumed in considerable quantities by delinquents.

In some situations, eliminating milk from the diet can result in dramatic improvements in behavior, especially in hyperactive children. Dr. Doris Rapp, clinical professor of pediatrics at the State University of New York at Buffalo, completed double-blind trials involving milk and other foods with hyperactive children. In four out of five children, aged 6 to 15, found to be sensitive to milk, all reported "markedly positive" improvements when milk was completely eliminated from the diet.[25] The fifth child reported "moderately positive" results.

Of course milk should still be considered a nutritious source of protein for children. Since the non-offender behaviorally disordered group in our study consumed an average of 27 ounces of milk a day, we do not suggest that delinquent children shouldn't drink milk. But our finding is surprising and calls for further study of a possible link between overconsumption of milk and delinquency. Research reported in the March, 1981, *Journal of Behavioral Ecology,* by the Law Enforcement Assistance Administration, U.S. Department of Justice, corroborates our discovered concern for milk consumption. In a program conducted by the San Luis Obispo (California) County Probation Department, juvenile offender's pre-natal, post-natal, and early childhood development were evaluated. Nearly 90 percent of the offenders had a symptom history associated with milk intolerance or allergy. Further physical examination and biochemical testing revealed 88 percent had evidence of milk allergy. One group of researchers reporting in the *Journal of Biological Chemistry* does suggest that a behavior disturbance might be manifested by milk due to some people's inability to break down the opoid peptides found in milk. Although unconfirmed and untested, such theoretical suggestions do point out the complexity of this issue.

B-1 Deficiency in Hostile Youths

Many juvenile offenders display the following personality traits: poor impulse control; easily angered; sensitive to criticism; easily irritated; and, usually hostile and aggressive. Correctional personnel know the difficulty of working with such youths. In February, 1980, Drs. Lonsdale and Shamberger reported in the *American Journal of Clinical Nutrition,* that such youths were found to be deficient in thiamine (Vitamin B-1), referring to this condition as sub-clinical beri-beri. These youths were found to overconsume high caloric junk foods rich in refined carbohydrates (sugar and white flour) missing such essential nutrients as thiamine. Thiamine is essential in breaking down carbohydrates so that we can benefit from the calories carbohydrates provide. The more carbohydrates one eats the more thiamine is required to metabolize it. When eating whole unprocessed carbohydrates nature provides the necessary thiamine in the right quantities to assist the body. Eating a diet rich in nutrient poor refined carbohydrates places extra demands on the body to provide the needed thiamine to metabolize the carbohydrates. If this persists over time, the end result is a thiamine deficiency.

Although the Recommended Daily Allowance (RDA) of thiamine is 1.5 mg (set by the National Research Council, National Academy of Sciences), in evaluating youths marked by the above personality traits, none in Lonsdale-Shamberger study had anywhere near the desired levels of thiamine. To correct this problem, the doctors gave each youth between 150 to 300 mg. of thiamine a day for three weeks while carefully monitoring when the thiamine levels in the blood would return to normal. At the end of three weeks the thiamine levels had reached the desired normal levels, but more important all of the personality traits we listed earlier disappeared! No longer were the youths hostile or agressive. The implications of this study are clear. Poor nutrition can have a very direct impact on the behavior and personality traits of offenders in the criminal justice system.

Lack of Training the Major Problem

When I spoke before both the National Juvenile Court and Family Judges Association and the California Legislature's Commission on Crime Control and Violence Prevention, members of both groups expressed a concern that criminal justice officials and schools were ill-equipped to diagnose or treat children and youths who have biochemical imbalances and break the law. They are correct. Through 1981 virtually no training of criminal justice officials exists in any English speaking country that draws upon the wealth of medical and scientific information potentially of practical value to such officials. With the exception of our American Institute for Biosocial Research course, Body Chemistry and Behavior, offered in four countries, there is no mechanism to train and expose criminal justice personnel to research having application in offender rehabilitation or crime prevention. Although this problem will be overcome in time, hundreds of thousands of offenders, potential offenders, and the public, must wait until change occurs.

Since 1978, thousands of health and social science professionals have completed the American Institute for Biosocial Research's courses.* This has begun to generate numerous programs that are finding offenders with the many problems discussed in this book.

Ms. Lynne M. Stout, a California probation officer who has completed course work in Body Chemistry and Behavior succinctly summarizes the two major points of such training:
"The body does not stop at the neck. Anything affecting the body also affects the brain. The brain is the center from which behavior is controlled. It therefore seems reasonable that anything which physically affects the individual can have some influence on his behavior.
Our body chemistry is affected by numerous environmental factors, including, but not limited to, what we eat, the air we breathe, the amount and quality of light to which we are exposed, the amount of exercise and rest we get, and the various stresses induced or influenced by social factors."
et us examine some of those factors affecting behavior, particularly criminal behavior, in the ensuing chapters.

*American Institute for Biosocial Research, Tacoma, Washington 98402

References

1. FOX, V. B. Delinquency and Its Treatment In Current Perspectives. Behavioral Disorders. 2: 5-15, August, 1975.
2. Sourcebook of Criminal Justice Statistics, 1978. U.S. Department of Justice, Law Enforcement Assistance Administration, National Criminal Justice Information and Statistics Service. Criminal Justice Research Center, Albany, New York.
3. Prisoners in State and Federal Institutions on December 31, 1978. National Prisoner Statistics Bulletin SD-NPS-PSF-6A, May, 1979. National Criminal Justice Information and Statistics Service, Law Enforcement Assistance Administration, U.S. Department of Justice.
4. Criminal Justice Newsletter, National Council on Crime and Delinquency. "Washington Report" 10(10): 4-5. Also, Congressional Record, April 25, 1979.
5. LYLE, William H. Jr. Temporary Insanity': Some Practical Considerations In a Legal Defense. J Orthomolecular Psychiatry. 8(3): 200, September, 1979.
6. TROJANOWICZ, R.C. Juvenile Delinquency: Concepts and Control. Prentice-Hall. Englewood Cliffs, New Jersey, 1973.
7. KVARACEUS, W.C. The Broken Home. In: Cavan, R. (ed.) Readings In Juvenile Delinquency. J.B. Lippincott. New York, 1969, pp. 187-188. Also, McCord, J. and McCord, W. The Effects of Parental Role Model In Community. In: Cavan, R. (ed.), ibid, pp. 176-186.
8. Hearing Before the Select Committee on Nutrition and Human Needs of the United States Senate, June 22, 1977. Statement of Mrs. Barbara Reed, Probation Officer, Cuyahoga Falls, Ohio. U. S. Government Printing Office. Washington, D.C., 1977, p. 57.
9. GROSS, Martin; The Psychological Society. Random House, New York, 1978. See, also: TENNOV, D. Psychotherapy: The Hazardous Cure. Abelard-Shuman, New York, 1975; PINCKNEY, E.R. and PINCKNEY, C. The Fallacy of Freud and Psychoanalysis. Prentice-Hall, Englewood Cliffs, N.J., 1965.
10. SCHAUSS, Alexander G. Orthomolecular Treatment of Criminal Offenders. Parker House, Berkeley, California, 1978, p. 29.
11. Personal Communication, 1979.
12. SCHAUSS, Alexander G. Differential Outcomes Among Probationers Comparing Orthomolecular Approaches to Conventional Casework/Counseling. J Orthomolecular Psychiatry. 8(3): 158-168, September, 1979. Paper presented at the Annual Meeting of the American Society of Criminology, Dallas, Texas, November 9, 1978.
13. D'ASARO, B., GROESBECK, C., and NIGRO, C. Diet-Vitamin Program for Jail Inmates. J Orthomolecular Psychiatry. 4(3): 212-222, 1975.
14. BAKER, Gene Orthomolecular System of Diet and Food Control. Memorandum from U.S. Naval Correctional Center, Naval Support Activity Center, Seattle, Washington, July 26, 1979.
15. Ibid., p. 1.
16. Personal Communication, 1978
17. Personal Communication, 1978
18. Personal Communication, 1979
19. Personal Communication, Alameda County Probation Department, 1979.
20. Personal Communication, 1979
21. Personal Communication, San Luis Obispo Probation Department, 1979.
22. SCHAUSS, Alexander G. and SIMONSEN, Clifford E. A. Critical Analysis of the Diets of Chronic Juvenile Offenders: Part I. J Orthom Psychiatry 8(3): 149-157, September, 1979

23. Ibid., p. 154.
24. SCHAUSS, Alexander G., BLAND, Jeffrey and SIMONSEN, Clifford E. A Critical Analysis of the Diets of Chronic Juvenile Offenders: Part II. J Orthom Psychiatry. 8(4): 222-226, December, 1979.
25. RAPP, Doris J. Food Allergy Treatment for Hyperkinesis. J Learning Disabilities. 12(9): 42-50, November, 1979.
26. ESLINGER, Marvin; Body Chemistry and Offender Behavior. California Correctional News 33(12): 9-10, December, 1979.
27. New Holistic Approach To Corrections. Washington Crime News Services' Corrections Digest. 10(26): 2-4, December 21, 1979; Jail Administrators Digest. 3(1): 3-5, January, 1980.

Bibliography

BONOMO, Joe (ed.) Carbohydrate Diet Guide. Bonomo Publications; New York, 1977.
CHERASKIN, E. and RINGSDORF, W. M. Jr. Psychodietetics. Stein and Day; Briarcliff, New York, 1974.
GIFFT, H.H., WASHBON, M.B. and HARRISON, G.G. Nutrition Behavior and Changes. Prentice-Hall; New York, 1972.
GILLETTE, Paul J. and HORNBECK, Marie, Psychochemistry. Warner Paperback Library; New York, 1974.
GROSS, Martin, The Psychological Society; A Critical Analysis of Psychiatry, Psychotherapy, Psychoanalysis and the Psychological Society. Random House; New York, 1978.
HAWKINS, David and PAULING, Linus (eds.) Orthomolecular Psychiatry. W.H. Freeman and Co.; San Francisco, 1973.
HIPPCHEN, Leonard J. (ed.) Ecologic-Biochemical Approaches to Treatment of Delinquents and Criminals. Van Nostrand Reinhold; New York, 1978.
HOFFER, Abram and WALKER, Morton; Orthomolecular Nutrition. Keats Publishing; New Canaan, Conn., 1978.
KIRSHMAN, John D. (ed.), Nutrition Almanac, revised ed. McGraw-Hill; New York, 1979.
LESSER, Michael; Nutrition and Vitamin Therapy. Grove Press, New York, 1980.
MACKARNESS, Richard; Eating Dangerously: The Hazards of Hidden Allergies. Harcourt Brace & Jovanovich; New York, 1976.
NEWBOLD, H.L. Mega-Nutrients. Peter W. Wyden; New York, 1975.
PFEIFFER, Carl; Mental and Elemental Nutrients. Keats Publishing; New Canaan, Conn., 1975.
PFEIFFER, Carl; Zinc and Other Micro-Nutrients. Keats Publishing; New Canaan, Connecticut, 1978.
PRICE, Weston A. Nutrition and Physical Degeneration. Price-Pottinger Nutrition Foundation, 5622 Dartford Way, San Diego, Ca. 92120, 1945.
RODALE, J.I. Natural Health, Sugar and the Criminal Mind. Pyramid Publications; New York, 1968.
ROE, Daphne A Plague of Corn: The Social History of Pellegra. AVI Publishers; Westport, Conn., 1973.
SCHAUSS, Alexander G. Orthomolecular Treatment of Criminal Offenders. Parker Press; Berkeley, California, 1978.

U.S. Government Printing Office. Diet Related To Killer Diseases, V: Nutrition and Mental Health Hearings Before the Senate Select Committee on Nutrition and Human Needs of the United States Senate (McGovern Committee). Request from Parker House; 2340 Parker St., Berkeley, California, 94704, "the Blue Book". 1980, $6.95 postage paid.

WALLACE, James F. and Maureen J. Effects of Excessive Consumption of Refined Sugar on Learning Skills, Behavior Attitudes and/or Physical Condition in School-Aged Children (pamphlet). Parents for Better Nutrition, 33 North Central, Rm. 200, Medford, Oregon 97501, 1978.

WATSON, George; Nutrition and Your Mind. Harper & Row; New York, 1972.

WILLIAMS, Roger J. Nutrition Against Disease. Pitman Publishing; New York, 1971.

WOOD, Curtis Jr. Overfed but Undernourished. Tower Publications; New York, 1971.

WURTMAN, R.J. and WURTMAN, J.J. (eds.) Nutrition and the Brain (3 volumes). Raven Press: New York, 1977, 1979.

FILMS & SLIDES

Dr. Price's Search For Health.

Price-Pottinger Nutrition Foundation
5622 Dartford Way
San Diego, Calif. 92120

Eat, Drink and Be Wary

Churchill Films
662 N. Robertson Blvd.
Los Angeles, Calif. 90069

II
LOW BLOOD SUGAR AND ANTISOCIAL BEHAVIOR

There is a vast medical literature suggesting the role blood sugar disorders can play in antisocial behavior. [1-34] The effects of low blood sugar on behavior have been reported in such journals as the *American Journal of Psychiatry*[35], *Journal of the American Medical Association* (JAMA)[36], the *British Medical Journal*[37], and the *British Journal of Psychiatry.*[38] The role blood sugar imbalances play in behavior has also received widespread attention. [39-51]

Dr. William Hudspeth, a researcher at the University of Nevada, Reno, has demonstrated that sugar can cause a whole range of behavioral symptoms, including depression, hyperactivity, and acting out behaviors that may be extremely asocial.[52]

Concern for the effects of sugar on behavior and health have risen as the amount of sugar consumed has increased. As can be seen in Figure 1., consumption of sugar in the United States has increased dramatically in the last 150 years. What effect this has on the central nervous system, and particularly children's health, is now receiving serious attention from such organizations as the American Public Health Association (APHA) and the U.S. Agriculture Department's Human Nutrition Center.[53] The APHA convened a panel of the nation's leading nutritionists in 1979. They concluded that over-consumption malnutrition[54] is a major health problem as children substitute snack and processed foods for traditional food staples. The results of these dietary habits are now being seen in increased incidences of obesity, high blood pressure, and hardening of the arteries, among a growing population of children.

It is estimated that one-tenth of the five billion dollars spent on food advertising is aimed directly at children. The average child watches over 25,000 commercials a year, more than half of them for food products. Dr. Louise Light, assistant to the administrator of the USDA's Human Nutrition Center, has warned that "children are particularly susceptible because they lack the maturity to consider commercials rationally."[55]

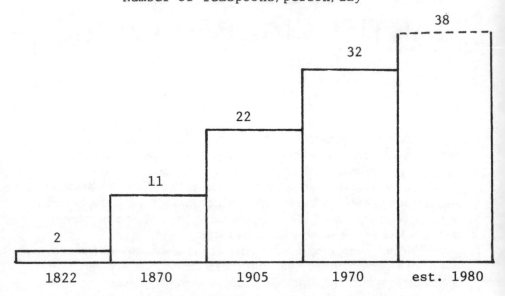

Figure 1.

TOTAL U.S. SUGAR CONSUMPTION

Number of Teaspoons/person/day

Source: National Food Situation 138, 1971.

Even in areas without television, like rural Peru, diets can play havoc on entire communities. Dr. Ralph Bolton describes his studies of the Qolla Indian society in rural Peru.[56] He labeled them the "meanest and most unlikeable people on earth." The majority of the Qolla reportedly engage in every form of criminal behavior, including murder, rape, arson, fighting and stealing. In one village of over 1,000 people, over 50 percent of the household heads were directly or indirectly implicated with homicide. Bolton tested the blood sugar of all males in the village and found that over 50 percent were clinically hypoglycemic (suffered from low blood sugar). Their diet was found to be very low in protein and excessively high in carbohydrates. To keep their blood sugar near normal, the villagers frequently fought, injured themselves, chewed cola or drank alcohol.

Dr. Abram Hoffer describes a case he handled with Dr. K. Thakur at City Hospital, Saskatoon, Saskatchewan, in 1975.[57]

"...a man had been in jail seven times over a ten-year period. In most cases he was thrown in jail because he liked to attack policemen. He was usually charged with disorderly conduct. He was not an alcoholic. When he was examined by Dr. Thakur he began to perspire profusely and suddenly he pulled out a two-pound jug full of sugar which he began to consume in large quantities. He told the doctor, 'this is the only thing that keeps me well.' He was tested and it was found he had severe relative hypoglycemia. He was placed on a diet and over the next ten-year period did not have any more difficulty.''

Dr. Seale Harris Defines Hypoglycemia

Hypoglycemia was first clinically described by Dr. Seale Harris in 1924 in the *Journal of the American Medical* Association.[58] A few years before Dr. Harris' report, the hormone insulin had been discovered and found effective in lowering the blood sugar of diabetics. But, if a diabetic received too much insulin, the blood sugar level fell excessively and the subject would feel nervous, tired, clammy and, in a few instances, have convulsions and faint. This is not surprising since the brain, although only two percent of the body by weight, uses close to 50 percent of all the available glucose or blood sugar in the blood. So any sudden changes in the blood sugar level would affect the brain. Dr. Harris noticed that some people would experience these same symptoms without receiving any insulin. He found if he gave these sufferers sugar, within a few minutes their symptoms would temporarily disappear. But sugar stimulated the body to release insulin, which in turn drove the blood sugar down, resulting in more symptoms of low blood sugar. Therefore, he concluded that these individuals had an abnormal insulin response to sugar (hyperinsulinism) resulting in low blood sugar.

The amount of sugar in the blood at any given time is controlled by the pancreas. When signaled by the brain that the sugar level is too high, the pancreas secretes insulin, which moves the blood sugar into the body's cells, bringing the blood sugar down to its proper level.

Dr. Harris found a high-protein low-sugar diet with frequent feedings effectively controlled hypoglycemia because it maintained a normal and stable blood sugar.[59] The American Medical Association awarded Dr. Harris a medal in recognition of his work.

It is now known that an adverse food reaction can also cause a significant drop in blood sugar if the person's endocrine (glandular) system is overreacting or dysfunctional. Ingestion of a food to which a person is allergic can cause a marked rise and later drop in the blood sugar. It is essential to understand that blood sugar imbalances can be caused by other factors than eating excessive sweets.

In the Nutrition Behavior Inventory [Appendix], 10 of the 50 questions provide presumptive evidence that a person might have a blood sugar disorder. The test's questions are graded according to severity: do the symptoms occur ''usually'', ''occasionally'', "rarely" or "never." The ten questions are:

1) I get headaches
2) My stomach or intestines are upset
3) I get faint, dizzy, have weak spells or cold sweats
4) I get very tired or exhausted
5) I often forget things
6) I feel very sleepy during the day
7) I feel depressed
8) I get depressed or feel the blues over nothing
9) I feel very nervous
10) I get drowsy

Persons responding "usually" or "occasionally" to four or more of the above ten items consistently show a high consumption of white sugar, refined carbohydrates, and caffeine. [60-62] Among chronic juvenile delinquents, this consumption has been as high as 75 hidden and 20 added teaspoons of refined sugar per day![63]

The Glucose Tolerance Test

Though presence of these symptoms leads me to suspect a blood sugar imbalance, the definite diagnosis can only be made when the person undergoes a five to six-hour Glucose Tolerance Test (GTT). The test is usually conducted in the morning after fasting from midnight the night before. A fasting blood sugar is drawn and then the person consumes a measured amount of glucose. Blood samples are then drawn hourly for the five to six-hour period. If the person has no problem with blood sugar imbalances, the fasting blood sugar level at the beginning of the test will be between 80 milligrams (mg) percent to 100 mg percent. Within the first hour after drinking the glucose solution, the blood sugar level should rise by at least 50 percent above the fasting level. By the second hour of the test, the blood sugar level should have returned to the fasting level. During the remaining three to four hours, the level should remain within an even range.

The level at which the blood sugar must drop to be considered low blood sugar varies. Some doctors do not consider the person hypoglycemic until the blood sugar drops below 50 mg percent. But I have worked with offenders whose blood sugar level never dropped below 60 mg percent, yet displayed severe hypoglycemic reactions. In one case, a young woman began cursing and screaming obscenities to the medical staff though her blood sugar only dropped to 70 mg percent. This was the same behavior observed by the arresting police officer.

What is more valuable to clinicians is the *relative* blood sugar drop (Figure 2.) Dr.'s Harvey Ross and H. Saltzer have developed the following criteria for judging a person as a relative hypoglycemic:

1) If any of the blood sugars fall more than 20 mg percent below the fasting level; *and*

2) If there is a fall of 50 mg percent or more in any one hour period, *accompanied by symptoms.*[64]

It is vital when performing the Glucose Tolerance Test that the doctor or technician observe the person for symptoms during the test. If the subject is diabetic or has severe hypoglycemia, the GTT may throw them into shock.

There is one other distinctive type of low blood sugar, *flat curve* hypoglycemia. Flat curve hypoglycemia is characterized by the failure of the blood sugar to rise by 50 percent from its fasting level during the first hour. When plotted on a graph (Figure 2.), the periodic levels appear more or less flat, hence the "flat curve."

Figure 2.

GLUCOSE TOLERANCE TEST

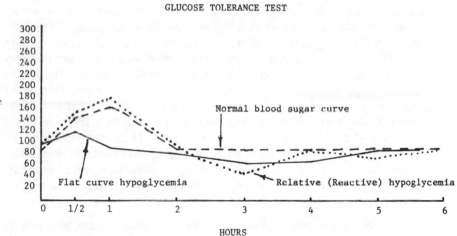

Among offenders who display this type of flat curve most prove very difficult to rehabilitate. They take months to respond to a change in diet. Frequently they are without energy, until the late evening hours, which is usually the time they got into trouble. This type of offender should probably be seen in the latter part of the day as they rarely seem responsive to counseling in the morning.

In summary, diagnosis of hypoglycemia is made if during the glucose tolerance test:

1) The blood sugar level drops by 20 mg percent or more below

the fasting level, accompanied by behavioral and/or physical symptoms at the time of the drop.

2) There is a drop in any hour period of at least 50 percent, accompanied by symptoms at the time of the drop.

3) Blood sugar fails to rise 50 percent above the fasting blood sugar level.

Certain people do not meet the above diagnostic criterion for hypoglycemia, yet exhibit symptoms of hypoglycemia and improve with a hypoglycemic diet. In some cases this may be due to the manner in which the test is conducted. One subject indicated to me that at the time he experienced a number of symptoms no blood was drawn. Blood should be drawn whenever symptoms appear or are reported by the person. By only drawing the scheduled hourly blood samples, a drop in the blood sugar might be missed.

Low Blood Sugar and Criminal Behavior

The Morristown, New Jersey, Rehabilitation Center studies suggested that low blood sugar can contribute to criminal behavior. Their first study revealed that Morristown inmates consumed much more refined sugar and caffeine than non-inmates.[65] They further concluded that many inmates were sugar addicts,[66] adding too much sugar to foods and eating a great deal of candy. They also drank large volumes of sugar-sweetened coffee and/or Kool-Aid (also high in sugar). Exactly the worst diet for a hypoglycemic. For this reason, they found that the long fasts common in most jails and prisons is "contraindicated in the treatment of hypoglycemia." [67] "In jails, as in most institutions, there is a long fast between the 5:00 p.m. dinner and the 7:00 a.m. breakfast. Inmates often buy candy bars to tide them over; sweets, of course, are banned in the diet to treat hypoglycemia."[68]

In countless numbers of prisons, jails and detention centers, I have observed the availability of coffee, sugar, candies and sweet drinks for confinees. In some institutions, the quantities of these substances is limitless. Little or no interest is shown in treating suspected hypoglycemia. Repeated studies have demonstrated an unusually high rate of hypoglycemia among offenders (averaging 80 to 85 percent), yet most correctional facility medical personnel still treat the problem as non-existent. The usual reponse is to prescribe medication when a delinquent or prisoner complains about dizziness, cold sweats, nervousness and fatigue--all potential signs of hypoglycemia.

The major recommendation to come out of the Morristown, New

Jersey, jail study of 1975 was that:

"Diet changes to treat existing hypoglycemia and diet education should be implemented immediately in jails and prisons."[69]

Unfortunately, for the estimated 310,000 prisoners and over one million juveniles detained in detention centers each year, it will take years before most correctional facilities in the United States will improve their diets to treat hypoglycemics.

Based on the reports of numerous physicians indicating a relationship between low blood sugar and criminal behavior, the experiences of the U.S. Naval Correctional Center in Seattle and the Morristown, New Jersey, jail study, it would seem reasonable that diet education and diet changes to treat hypoglycemia be implemented in all correctional facilities.

Sugar Is Added To Many Foods

It is often difficult to determine the amount of sugar in various processed foods. Mrs. Sara Sloan, Director of Food Services for the Fulton County Schools in Georgia, provides school children the following list of foods[70] which have added sugar:

Apple Butter
Breath Mints
Brownies
Butterscotch Sauce
Cake of any kind
Candy of any kind
Carmel Sauce
Carnation Breakfast Bar
Catsup
Cereals (sugar coated)
Chocolate Sauce
Chocolate Milk
Cobblers (apple, cherry, etc.)
Cocoa
Cocoa Malt
Condensed Milk
Cough Drops, Cough Syrup
Cracker Jacks
Custard
Doughnuts
Dried Fruits of any kind
Eggnog
Fiddle Faddle, Screaming Yellow
   Zonkers
Figurines
Frosting
Fruit Cake

Jelly, Jam, Marmalade
Ice Cream (Bars, Cones)
Instant Breakfast
Kool-Aid
Lemonade
Licorice
Marshmallows
Milk Shake
Molasses
Peanut Butter with sugar
Pies of all types
Popsicles
Pop Tarts, similar foods
Puddings
Rolaids
Sherbert
Soft Drinks
Space Food Stick
Stewed Sweetened Fruits
Sweetened Carbonated Beverages
Sweetened Mayonnaise
Syrup of all types
Tang
Tomato Sauce
Vegetables canned with sugar
Wine (red wine)
Yogurt - fruit flavored

Fruit Cocktail
Fruits canned in heavy syrup
Granola Crunch Bars
Hawaiian Punch Drink

Yogurt - frozen
Fruit flavored gelatin (Jello)
Gum
Hi-C Juice

To determine whether a food has sugar, it is important to read the labels on cans, boxes or containers. This does not inform you as to how much sugar is contained therein. Avoid packaged foods with labels indicating the presence of sugar, corn syrup, "brown" sugar, turbinado sugar, raw sugar, or "refined" sugar. If the package label indicates a sugar to be the first ingredient, this means that it is in greatest abundance in the food or beverage.

In the next chapter another sweet tasting substance, lead, will be examined for its role in affecting impaired behavior.

References

1. ADLERSBERG, D. and DOLGER, H. Medico-legal Problems of Hypoglycemia Reactions in Diabetes. Ann Int Med. 12: 1804-1815, 1938.
2. BOVILL, D. A Case of Functional Hypoglycemia-a Medico-legal Problem. Brit J Psych. 123: 353-358, 1973.
3. BUCKLEY, R.E. Hypoglycemic Symptoms and the Hypoglycemic Experience. Psychosomatics. 10: 7-13, 1969.
4. CONN, J.W. The Diagnosis and Management of Spontaneous Hypoglycemia. J Am Med A. 134: 130-137, 1947.
5. DUNCAN, G.G. The Antidotal Effect of Anger in a Case of Insulin Reaction (Hypoglycemia) in a Diabetic. Canadian Med Assoc J 33-71, 1935.
6. FREINKEL, N., ARKY, R.A., SINGER, D.L. COHEN, A.K., BLEICHER, S. J., ANDERSON, J.B., SILBERT C.K., FOSTER, A.E. Alcohol Hypoglycemia IV: Current Concepts of its Pathogenesis. Diabetes, 14(6): 350-361, 1965.
7. GITTLER, R.D. Spontaneous Hypoglycemia. New York State J Medicine 62: 236-250, 1962.
8. GREENWOOD, J. Hypoglycemia as a Cause of Mental Symptoms. Penn Med J 39: 12-16, 1935.
9. HARRIS, S. Hyperinsulinism and Dysinsulinism. J Am Med Assoc (JAMA) 83: 729-733, 1924.
10. HARRIS, S. The Diagnosis and Treatment of Hyperinsulinism. Annals of Internal Med. 10: 514-533, 1936.
11. HEATH, F.K. Hypoglycemia: Combined Staff Clinics. Am J Med. 1: 412-427, 1946.
12. HIMWICH, H.E. A Review of Hypoglycemia, its Physiology and Pathology, Symptomatology and Treatment. Am J Digestive Diseases. 11: 1-8, 1944.
13. HILL, d. SARGANT, W., and HEPPENSTALL, M. A. Case of Matricide. The Lancet. 526-527, April 24, 1943.
14. HOFELDT, F.D. Reactive Hypoglycemia. Metabolism: Clinical and Experimental. 24(10): 1193-1208, 1975.
15. JONES, M.S. Hypoglycemia in the Neuroses. British Medical Journal 2: 945-946, 1935.
16. KEPLER, E.J. and MOERSCH, F.P. The Psychiatric Manifestations of Hypoglycemia. Am J Psychiatry. 17:89-109, 1937.
17. LANDMANN, H.R. The Differential Diagnosis of Hypoglycemia. AM J Digestive Diseases. 19: 110-112, 1952.
18. LIBERMAN, A.A. Nervous and Mental Manifestations Observed in Spontaneous Hypoglycemia. Illinois Med J. 85: 287-292, 1944.
19. LIU, S.H. and CHANG-ISIAO, C. Hypoglycemia in a Case Unassociated with Insulinism Administration. Archives Internal Med. 36: 146, 1925.
20. MASTERS, H.R. Sugar Metabolism: Its Symptomatic Relation To Neurologic and Psychiatric Disorders. Southern Ned J. 28: 256-258, 1935.
21. McCARRISON, R. Studies in Deficiency Disease. Hazell, Watson and Viney Ltd., London, 1921.
22. PODOLSKY, E. The Chemical Brew of Criminal Behavior. J Crim Law, Crim Pol Sci. 45: 675-678, 1955.
23. PODOLSKY, E. The Chemistry of Murder. Pakistan Med J. 15: 9-14, 1964.
24. POWELL, E. The Role of Diet in the Etiology and Treatment of Mental Disorders Resulting from Hyperinsulinism. Tri-State Med J. 1323-1333, July, 1934.
25. RUD, E. Spontaneous Hypoglycemia with Peculiar Psychic Disturbances. Acta Scandinavia. 91: 648-655, 1937.

26. RYNEARSON, E.H. and MOERSCH, F.P. Neurologic Manifestations of Hyperinsulinism and Other Hypoglycemic States. J Am Med Assoc (JAMA). 103: 1196-1198, 1934.
27. SCHLAPP, M. and SMITH, E.E. The New Criminology: A Consideration of the Chemical Causation of Abnormal Behavior. Boni and Liveright, New York, 1928.
28. VONDERAHE, A.R. Personality Change in Hypoglycemia. Cincinnati J Med. 17: 189-190, 1936.
29. WAUCHOPE, J. Critical Review: Hypoglycemia. Quarterly J Med. 2: 117-160, 1933.
30. WILDER, J. Problems of Criminal Psychology Related to Hypoglycemic States, J Criminal Psychopathology. 1: 219, 233, 1940.
31. WILDER, J. Psychological Problems in Hypoglycemia. Am J Digestive Diseases. 10: 428, 435, 1943.
32. WILDER, J. Sugar Metabolism in its Relation to Criminology. In: LINDNER, R.M. and SELIGER, R.V. Handbook of Correctional Psychology. Philosophical Library, New York, 1947.
33. YARYURA-TOBIAS, J.A. and NEZIROGLU, F. Violent Behavior, Brain Dysrhythmia and Glucose Dysfunction, A New Syndrome. J Orthomolecular Psychiatry. 4: 182-188, 1975.
34. ZIEGLER. L.H. Disturbances of Sleep and Maniacal Delirium Associated with Spontaneously Low Blood Sugar. Medical Clinics of North America. pp. 1363-1367, May, 1930.
35. KEPLER, E.J. and MOERSCH, F.P. The Psychiatric Manifestations of Hypoglycemia. Am J Psychiatry. 17: 89-109, 1937.
36. CONN, J.W. The Diagnosis and Management of Spontaneous Hypoglycemia. JAMA. 134: 130-137, 1947.
37. JONES, M.S. Hypoglycemia in the Neuroses. British Med J. 2: 945-946, 1935.
38. BOVILL, D. A Case of Functional Hypoglycemia - a Medico-legal Problem. British J Psychiatry. 123: 353-358, 1973.
39. GOODHART, R.S. The Role of Nutritional Factors in the Cause, Prevention and Cure of Alcoholism and Associated Infirmities. Am J Clinical Nutrition. 5: 613, 1957.
40. D'ASARO, B., et al. Polyamine Levels in Jail Inmates. J Orthomolecular Psychiatry. 4(2): 149-152, 1975.
41. NEWBOLD, H.L. Mega-Nutrients for Your Nerves. Peter H. Wyden, New York, 1975.
42. FREDERICKS, Carlton, Psycho-Nutrition. Grosset & Dunlap. New York, 1976.
43. ADAMS, R. and MURRAY, F. Megavitamin Therapy. Larchmont Books, New York, 1973.
44. SCHNEOUR, E. The Malnourished Mind. Anchor-Doubleday, New York, 1974.
45. PALMER, L. Early Childhood Caffeine and Sugar Habituation. J Orthomolecular Psychiatry. 6(3): 248-250, 1977.
46. THOMSON, C.A. and POLLITT, E. Effects of Severe Calorie Malnutrition on Behavior in Human Populations. In: GREENE, Lawrence S. (ed.) Malnutrition, Behavior and Social Organization. Academic Press, New York, 1977.
47. PRICE, Weston A. Nutrition and Physical Degeneration. The Price-Pottinger Nutrition Foundation, Santa Monica, Ca., 1945.
48. PHILPOTT, W.H. The Physiology of Violence: The Role of Central Nervous System
Maladaptive Responses to Foods and Chemicals in Evoking Antisocial and Violent Behaviors. In; Hippchen, Leonard (ed.) The Ecologic-Biochemical Approaches to Treatment of Delinquents and Criminals. Van Nostrand-Reinhold, New York, 1978.

49. YARYURA-TOBIAS, J.A. Biological Research on Violent Behavior. In: Hippchen Leonard (ed.) The Ecologic-Biochemical Approaches to Treatment of Delinquents and Criminals. Van Nostrand-Reinhold, New York, 1978.

50. YARYURA-TOBIAS, J.A. and NEZIROGLU, F.A. Violent Behavior, Brain Dysthythmia, and Glucose Dysfunction, a New Syndrome. J Orthomolecular Psych 4(3): 182-188, 1975.

51. CHERASKIN, E. and RINGSDORF, W.M. Jr. Psycho-Dietetics. Stein and Day, New York, 1974.

52. Dr. William Hudspeth, Department of Behavioral Science and Psychiatry, School of Medicine, University of Nevada, Reno, has been doing research on the effect of sugar and hypoglycemia on human brain waves.

53. Poor Nutrition Blamed On Junk Food. Associated Press (AP) coverage of the American Public Health Association's December 19, 1979, meeting in New York City. December 21, 1979.

54. WOOD, Durtis Jr. Overfed but Undernourished. Tower Publications; New York, 1971.

55. Poor Nutrition Blamed On Junk Food, ibid.

56. BOLTON, R. Aggression in Qolla Society. Garland Press. Champaign, Ill., 1978.

57. HOFFER, Abram Behavioral Nutrition. J Othomolecular Psychiatry. 8(3): 174, 1979.

58. HARRIS, Seale, Hyperinsulinism and Dysinsulinism. J AM Med Assoc (JAMA) 83: 729-733, 1924.

59. The argument over terminology concerning blood sugar levels could be eliminated if hypoglycemia would be referred to as "nutritionally induced chronic endocrinopathy". This phrase more accurately describes blood sugar disorders that are nutritionally related.

60. ROSS, Harvey M. Fighting Depression. Larchmont Books, New York, 1975.

61. CHERASKIN, E. and RINGSDORF, W.M. Jr. Psycho-Dietetics. Stein and Day, New York, 1974.

62. YUDKIN, John, Sweet and Dangerous. Peter H. Wyden, New York, 1972.

63. SCHAUSS, Alexander G., BLAND, Jeffrey, and SIMONSEN, Clifford E. A Critical Analysis of the Diets of Chronic Juvenile Offenders: Part II. J Orthomolecular Psychiatry. 8(4), December, 1979.

64. ROSS, Harvey M. Fighting Depression. Larchmont Books, New York, 1975, p. 89.

65. D'ASARO, B. Dietary Habits in Jail Inmates. Report of Morris County Jail Rehabilitation Program. Sheriff's Office, Morristown, New Jersey, November, 1973. See, J Orthom Psych, 4(3): 212-222, 1975.

66. D'ASARO, B., GROESBECK, C. and NIGRO, C. Diet-Vitamin Program for Jail Inmates. J Orthomolecular Psyciatry. 4(3): 212-222, 1975.

67. Ibid, p. 214. (footnote 10).

68. Ibid, p. 214. (footnote 10).

69. Ibid, p. 221.

70. SLOAN, Sara, Is Nutrition Served At Your School? Fulton County Schools, Atlanta, Georgia 30315. 1979, p. 14.

Bibliography

ABRAHAMSON, E.M. and PEZET, A.W. Body, Mind and Sugar. Holt, Reinhart and Winston; New York, 1951.

ADAMS, Ruth and MURRAY, Frank, Body, Mind and the B Vitamins. Larchmont Books; New York, 1975.

ADAMS, Ruth and MURRAY, Frank, Is Low Blood Sugar Making You A Nutritional Cripple? Larchmont Books: New York, 1970.

CHERASKIN, E and RINGDORF, W.M. Jr. Psychodietetics. Stein and Day; Briarcliff, New York, 1974.

CLARK, Linda, Know Your Nutrition. Keats Publishing; New Canaan, Conn., 1973.

CLEAVE,. T.I. The Saccharine Disease. Keats Publishing; New Canaan, Conn., 1975.

CLEAVE, T.L., CAMPBELL, G.D. and PAINTER, N.S. Diabetes, Coronary Thrombosis, and the Saccharine Disease, 2nd ed. John Wright & Sons; Bristol, London, 1969.

DUFTY, William, Sugar Blues. Warner Books; New York, 1975.

FREDERICKS, Carlton, Psycho-Nutrition. Grosset & Dunlap; New York, 1976.

GILLETTE, Paul J. and HORNBECK, Marie, Psychochemistry. Warner Paperback Library; New York, 1974.

HAWKINS, David and PAULING, Linus (eds.) Orthomolecular Psychiatry. W.H. Freeman and Co.; San Francisco, 1973.

HIPPCHEN, Leonard J. (ed.) Ecologic-Biochemical Approaches to Treatment of Delinquents and Criminals. Van Nostrand Reinhold; New York, 1978.

HOFFER, Abram and WALKER, Morton, Orthomolecular Nutrition. Keats Publishing; New Canaan, Connecticut, 1978.

KIRSCHMAN, John D. (ed.) Nutrition-Almanac, Revised Edition. McGraw-Hill Book Company; New York, 1979.

LESSER, Michael, Nutrition and Vitamin Therapy. (Chapter Nine, Neurosis and Blood Sugar;) Grove Press; New York, 1980.

PRICE, Weston A. Nutrition and Physical Degeneration. Price-Pottinger Nutrition Foundation, 5622 Dartford Way, San Diego, Ca. 92120, 1945.

RODALE, J.I. Natural Health, Sugar and the Criminal Mind. Pyramid Publications; New York, 1968.

ROSS, Harvey, Fighting Depression. Larchmont Books; New York, 1975.

STEINCHROHN, Peter J. Low Blood Sugar. Henry Renery Co; Chicago, 1972.

U. S. Government Printing Office, Dietary Goals for the United States, 2nd Ed. Senate Select Committee on Nutrition and Human Needs; McGovern Committee. Stock Number 070-04376-8, December, 1977.

WADE, Carlson, Emotional Health and Nutrition. Award Books; New York, 1971.

WALLACE, James F. and Maureen J. Effects of Excessive Consumption of Refined Sugar on Learning Skills, Behavior Attitudes and/or Physical Condition in School-Aged Children (pamphlet). Parents for Better Nutrition, Medford, Oregon, 1978.

WATSON, George, Nutrition and Your Mind. Harper & Row; New York, 1972.

WILLIAMS, Roger, The Wonderful World Within You. Bantam Books; New York, 1977.

WOOD, Curtis Jr. Overfed and Undernourished. Tower Publications; New York, 1971.

YUDKIN, John, Sweet and Dangerous. Peter H. Wyden; New York, 1972.

Films & Slides

Eat, Drink and Be Wary (film)

Churchill Films
662 N. Robertson Blvd.
Los Angeles, Calif. 90069

Pottinger Cat Studies (film)
Dr. Price's Search For Health (film)

Price-Pottinger Nutrition Foundation
5622 Dartford Way
San Diego, Calif. 92120

The Sugar Film

Image Associates, Inc.
P. O. Box 40106, 352 Conejo Road
Santa Barbara, Ca. 93103

The Living Tooth (slides w/audible)
Sugartime (slides w/audible)

Professional Health Media Services
P. O. Box 922
Loma Linda, Ca. 92354

Sweet, White & Deadly (slides w/audible)

Photo Sound International, inc.
4151 Memorial Drive, #101-E
Decatur, Georgia 30032

III
LEAD, BEHAVIOR AND CRIMINALITY

The lead levels in modern man may be over 500 times greater than that of 350 years ago. Lead levels formerly considered safe have recently been shown to increase abnormal behavior, cause learning difficulties and reduce intelligence.

Lead is a highly toxic trace mineral that occurs naturally in the earth's crust. For the last several centuries, human exposure to lead poisoning has increased in magnitude[1] because massive quantities have been released into our environment as a result of industrial activity.

It has been estimated that the human body can only tolerate about .00003 ounces (one milligram) of lead without suffering toxic side effects.[2] That amount is the equivalent of two pounds of food contaminated with only one part per million of lead.[3] In an urban environment, the average person ingests with solid foods one milligram of lead per week.[4] A further fifth of a milligram of lead comes from beverages.[5] The World Health Organization (WHO) estimates only ten percent of the lead ingested is actually absorbed by the body (.12 milligram).

Lead is also accumulated in the body by inhalation, mainly from auto exhaust. The typical inhalation of airborne lead at urban sites not close to heavy traffic, lead smelters, etc., is slightly less than one fifth of a milligram per day.[6] Only 40 percent of the airborne lead inhaled is actually absorbed (.08 milligram).[7]

Thus, a person living in an urban area, not close to heavy traffic, lead smelters, etc., absorbs about one-tenth the amount of lead needed to induce toxic effects. It's estimated we can excrete only half a milligram of lead a day and, even with intakes well below that level, lead slowly builds up in tissue and bone.[7]

Researchers have found that the dietary absorption and retention of lead is much higher in children than in adults. In a 1978 issue of *Pediatric Research*, Dr. E.E. Ziegler concluded:

"There is little question that infants and young children absorb and retain a greater percentage of ingested lead than has been reported for adults."[8]

These findings have been confirmed by numerous scientists who estimate that children absorb lead up to ten times more efficiently than adults. [9-14]

Tony, A Case of Lead Poisoning

Tony, aged 21, was being held in county jail. He had been arrested for battering a police officer, creating a public disturbance, resisting arrest and reckless driving. During his court arraignment, he was disoriented, disruptive and completely irrational. Given his mental condition, the judge ordered the probation department to evaluate the man's ability to remain locked up in the county jail. A psychiatrist and the probation department's mental health specialist interviewed the subject over a three-day period. The psychiatrist diagnosed the man as "acutely schizophrenic", while the mental health specialist asserted he was a full-blown "paranoid schizophrenic." Both predicted that his condition would continue to deteriorate with age. The probation officer was informed that Tony would become a "vegetable" by the age of 30. Because of his long criminal record (starting at the age of 11), Tony was held in jail while the probation department prepared its recommendation to the court.

Tony's probation officer suspected his bizarre behavior might be due to lead poisoning. The consulting physician ran blood, urine and hair tests which confirmed the toxic body burdens of lead, while also finding high concentrations of mercury, cadmium and arsenic.

Tony's mother revealed that when he was a little boy he ate mostly refined foods and consumed oysters and clams from nearby beaches. At that time the family lived down wind from a large metal refinery that released toxic heavy metals in abundance. She went on to state that when he was in elementary school, school authorities labeled him both learning disabled and behaviorally disordered.[15]

Learning Difficulties and Lead

In 1978, Dr. R.O. Pihl, Professor at McGill University in Canada, reported he could select out learning disabled and behaviorally disordered school children with nearly 98 percent accuracy just by reviewing the levels of several elevated minerals and metals, including lead and cadmium.[16]

Dr. Herbert Needleman et al, reported in a 1979 issue of the *New England Journal of Medicine* that evidence existed of a lead-behavior-learning triad after 2,146 school children's shed teeth were examined. [17-18] This study by Boston's Children's Hospital Medical Center and Harvard Medical School revealed the following:

1) Children with high lead levels appeared particularly less competent in areas of verbal performance and auditory processing.
2) The ability of subjects with high lead levels to sustain attention was clearly impaired.
3) Teachers' reports of classroom behavior showed that children with high lead levels reported significantly poorer on eight of ten items. Behaviors common to the higher lead children were:

   a) Distractibility
   b) Lacking in persistence
   c) Constantly dependent and clinging
   d) Impulsiveness
   e) Easily become frustrated
   f) Daydreaming
   g) Fail to follow simple directions
   h) Fail to follow sequence of directions

4) Children with high lead levels preformed significantly poorer on the Weschler Intelligence Scale for Children (WISC-Revised), especially on verbal items and three measures of auditory and verbal processing.

Dr. Needleman concludes that "the impaired function of children with high lead levels, demonstrated in the neuropsychologic laboratory, mirrored by disordered classroom behavior, appears to be an adverse effect of exposure to lead."[19] The eight behavioral items the high lead children performed poorest in are often found in children labeled as hyperactive or hyperkinetic. The relationship between lead levels and hyperactivity have been reported in both the *Journal of Pediatrics*[20] and the *American Journal of Diseases in Children.*[21] These studies have been confirmed in Sweden, Switzerland, and most notably by Professor Derek Bryce-Smith at the University of Reading in England. [22-23] It was Dr. Bryce-Smith's profound paper, "Lead, Behaviour and Criminality"[24], that heightened my interest in the role of heavy metals and criminal behavior.

Significantly, Needleman discovered that the lead levels found to affect the school children's behavior was *below* the usually considered toxic levels. Government standards for lead felt to be safe for children were, in fact, not safe. This led Dr. Needleman to conclude, "Permissible exposure levels of lead for children deserve reexamination in the light of these data."[25]

A 1977 report by the New York City Department of Health's Bureau of Lead Poisoning Control estimated that 275,000 children in that city were at risk for "lead intoxication and frank lead poisoning."[26] The report supports Dr. Needleman's finding by stating, "While these children do not appear to be sick, there is increasing documentation that they are being subtly impaired and prevented from obtaining their full potential."

The Link Between Learning And/Or Behavior Disorder And Delinquency

Children can absorb enough lead to impair their performance on tests of reasoning, coordination, intelligence and reading. These conclusions are more alarming when evaluating the reported correlations between learning and/or behaviorally disordered children (LD or BD) and juvenile delinquency (JD). The incidence rates between JD and LD or BD have been reported from between 32 to 90 percent. [27-29]

Donna Sawicki and Beatrix Schaeffer, St. Louis (Missouri) Juvenile Court, provide two "basic rationales" in support of the LD-BD/JD link in the *Juvenile & Family Court Journal*.[30]

The first rationale is the School Failure Rationale which is based upon the labeling process. Here the student is labeled as a problem with the result being a negative self-image. The second, the Susceptibility Rationale comes about, according to Sawicki and Schaeffer, when the child shows "general impulsiveness, an apparent poor ability to learn from experience, and a poor perception of social cues." Whether one "rationale" seems more plausible than the other, the bottom line is that the LD-BD child is less receptive to the usual social sanctions and rewards of our society and, therefore, develops an increased susceptibility for criminal behavior.

If lead can interfere with learning, is it realistic to expect a youth in high school with third grade academic skills to become a productive member of our society?

Data from the Clinical Ecology Treatment Program of the San Luis Obispo County Juvenile Probation Department in California provides evidence of the lead/LD-BD/JD link. Among 20 medically and educationally screened juvenile delinquents, 70 percent were found to be learning disabled (two or more grades behind) and 60 percent had lead levels above 11 parts per million (ppm).[31] Virtually all of the LD clients had lead levels ranging from 11 ppm to 35 ppm.

To study the effects of low-level sources of lead, the National Institute of Environmental Health Sciences funded a multidisciplinary team in 1976 to investigate how chronic lead intake affected a group of Philadelphia children who had no symptoms of lead poisoning. They found that those children with the lowest level of lead had an average IQ of 97, while those with the highest levels averaged 80. Boys with the higher lead levels had deficits in simple math calculations and visual-motor coordination. Girls with the higher lead levels scored poorer in memory, abstracting and visual searching.[32]

Lead and Behavior

In the 18th century Kingdom of the Kongo, Bakongo tribesmen wore heavy ornaments of copper, tin and lead. The Bakongo regarded these metals as very precious substances and forged them into amulets and bracelets to be worn by those tribesmen of higher rank. From wearing the lead bracelets and amulets some of the tribe developed lead poisoning. The tribesmen so afflicted would act either manic, drowsy, irritable, or even aggressive. To treat this lead poisoning, ''the Bakongo devised preventive and curative methods both pharmacological (massive doses of pawpaw and palm oil) and mechanical.''[33] As George Balandier wrote in *Daily Life in the Kingdom of the Kongo,* these methods of combatting lead poisoning became the tribe's way of using knowledge to keep one step ahead of technology.

Unfortunately, our society's ability to stay one step ahead of technology appears to be a losing battle. Too much lead has and is being released into our environment. It affects everyone, regardless of social importance. The negative results can be illustrated by the following case.

A family on the West coast is suffering from fatigue and depression. Inexplicably, all four members of the family show the same symptoms. In addition, the children exhibited behavioral changes; their school work became poor and they experienced sharp mood swings. Their family physician found no apparent physical basis for the problems and referred them to a psychiatrist.

After spending several thousand dollars, they saw no improvement.

Conceiving that their diet might be a cause of their suffering, and reading about lead poisoning in a popular magazine, they visited a nutritionist. A review of their diet revealed nothing. However, the nutritionist took samples of their hair, clipped from the nape of the neck, for laboratory analysis. The results revealed the family had lead poisoning!

The family physician, having seen no visible evidence of lead toxicity, had not ordered a blood test for lead poisoning. A search was made to find the cause of their lead poisoning, which was traced to an extremely high lead content in the glaze of the family's china! When the suggestion was made to dispose of the china, the father commented, "That china cost $25 a plate."

Symptoms of Lead Toxicity:

Dr. Gary F. Gordon, has listed the following signs and symptoms of lead toxicity.[34]

Central Nervous System: Hyperactivity, mild neurological disability, perceptual disorders, headache, insomnia, emotional instability, loss of coordination, restlessness, vertigo, clumsiness, confusion, depression and, in younger children, mental retardation. Lead can also be transmitted to the child by its mother through the placenta (ie., transplacental lead).

Abdominal or Gastro-intestinal: Diarrhea, loss of appetite, abdominal colic or cramping, loss of weight, constipation, malaise and nausea.

Neuromuscular: Fatigue, muscular discomfort and weakness, gout and atrophy. It can also include degeneration of motor neurons and axons.

Other Signs: General signs of diminished vitality, difficulty handling stress, impaired kidney function, irritability, episodic vomiting, and in severe cases, lead encephalopathy or brain damage.

Common In Children: Hyperactivity, temper tantrums, withdrawals, frequent crying for no apparent reason, fearfulness, refusal to play, drowsiness, learning disabilities, speech disturbances, perceptual motor dysfunctions, seizures or convulsions, ataxia, and emotional or behavioral problems.[90]

During a workshop for inmates on diet and behavior at a state women's prison, I asked the inmates to list their most frequent physical and mental complaints. All 30 women listed symptoms commonly associated with high lead levels. None had ever had their lead levels checked.

Removing Body Lead:

Chelation:

Chelate from the Greek, means "to claw". A chelating agent is a chemical introduced into the body because of its ability to combine with toxic metals, such as lead, forming compounds which are readily eliminated from the body.

Aside from the more expensive and potentially toxic chelating drugs, such as EDTA (ethylene diaminetetracetic acid), penicillamine, and acetylcysteine, certain nutrients have the capacity to either directly chelate toxic metals or facilitate the body's natural ability to remove these poisons. The choice of whether to use chelating agents or foods and nutrient supplements depends upon the levels of lead in the body and the judgement of the physician.

Dietary Measures':

Using foods and/or nutritional supplements to remove lead is slower than drug chelation but safer because it does not overwork the kidneys or risk sudden removal of desirable minerals, such as calcium, which must then be replaced.

There are a variety of nutrients in foods that have the ability to chelate toxic metals. The amino acids, methionine, cysteine and cystine, contain sulfhydryl compounds, which are natural chelators. Therefore, food rich in these compounds, such as beans, eggs, onions and garlic, help remove toxic metals. Since it requires large quantities of these food to have a significant impact on the body's toxic metal burden, it is often more desirable to use specific nutritional supplements.

Vitamin C is such a supplement, which according to Dr. Alsoph H. Corwin, Emeritus Professor of Chemistry, John Hopkins University, does not itself ordinarily act as a chelator.[35] Rather, vitamin C facilitates the body's natural ability to remove heavy metals, by excretion through the kidneys.[36] For vitamin C to perform as a chelating agent, a person would need to consume at least 3,000 milligrams daily, (three fourths of a teaspoon of vitamin C powder), states Dr. Corwin.

Alginate (algin) is a non-nutritious chelating substance found abundantly in Pacific kelp (seaweed).[37] it is taken as a supplement in the form of sodium alginate.

Dietary fiber acts to speed the intestinal transit time of food, and consequently any ingested toxic metals; thereby reducing absorption of these poisons into the body. Cereal brans are good sources of fiber, but the refining of cereals has removed much of the fiber from the diets of persons living in industrialized countries.

Constipation and other problems of a low residue diet are rarely seen in primitive peoples eating a high fiber diet, notes epidemiologist Dr. Denis Burkitt. Possibly the reason Orientals have lower toxic metal levels than Occidentals is partly because their diets are richer in kelp and fiber.

Pectin, found abundantly in apples, binds with toxic metals and assists in their elimination. Dr. Glenn H. Joseph reports in *Nutrition Research* that during digestion, pectin is transformed into galactouronic acid, a cleansing agent which combines with lead to form an insoluble metallic salt. Since the salt cannot be absorbed from the gut, it passes out with the stool.

Increasing the dietary intake of calcium and phosphorous reduces the absorption of lead. [38-41] In laboratory animals, low dietary intake of calcium and phosphorous increases gastrointestinal absorption of lead, heightens the retention of lead and facilitates its mobilization from bone to soft tissue. Jerry Knight, director of the Court Clinic Research Foundation in Chicago, has found that offenders with high lead levels all show low levels of calcium.[42]

Low levels of zinc, copper and iron may facilitate the absorption of lead. In 1972, Drs. Niklowitz and Yeager exposed rats to the forms of lead that come from automobile exhaust: tetra-ethyl lead, tetra-methyl lead and tetra-alkyl lead.[43] Although tetra-alkyl lead accounts for less than one percent of automobile and truck exhausts (when lead gasoline is used), even small amounts can damage the brain and central nervous system.[44] Drs. Nicklowitz and Yeager analyzed the brains of the lead-exposed rats for the common trace elements zinc, copper and iron. All three elements were found to be significantly decreased by lead exposure. Zinc, copper and iron are necessary for a large number of important enzymes which regulate mental processes.[45]

Numerous vitamin houses provide combination detoxification supplements containing vitamin C, sodium alginate, l-cystine, dl-methionine, pectin, and other important nutrients. But even if you take these supplements, you must still eat a well balanced diet.

Before explaining how you can determine whether you have elevated levels of toxic metals in your body, let us examine the potential sources of lead.

Potential Lead Sources

Understanding lead poisoning and eating foods that reduce lead levels does not eliminate the problem of lead exposure. The following is a list of potential sources of lead:[46]

lead smelters	spitballs	vegetables growing by roadside
leaded gasoline exhaust	cosmetics (i.e., mascara)	hair colorings (to remove grey)
storage batteries	cigarettes	pencils (paint)
porcelain enamels	pottery glazes	plaster and putty
dirt and dust	heavy duty greases	painted glassware
newsprint	solder	children's toys
varnishes	lead pipes	linotype metals
pigments	bullets, lead shot	products with metal parts
paints (yes, they still have lead)		containing lead

These potential sources of lead should be reduced or eliminated if it is discovered that a person has unacceptably high levels of lead.

Old deteriorated housing built before World War II has been a particularly important cause of lead poisoning in children. Prior to World War II, most paints were 40 to 80 percent pure lead. This paint eventually peels and contaminates the dust, which is then inhaled by the home's residents. In a Cleveland, Ohio, study, 27 percent of the young children living in urban housing showed increased lead.[47] In Baltimore, over 50 percent of the old houses in selected slum areas contained flaking lead paints at unsafe levels.[48] Because lead is as sweet tasting to young childen as sugar, many youngsters and babies intentionally ingest lead paint chips unaware of its long-term consequences. Only a few flakes of peeled paint may contain over 100 milligrams of lead!

With the exception of the Full Circle School[49], a residential treatment facility in Bolinas, California, and a pilot project at the San Bernardino County Probation Department in California, I know of no other correctional programs in the United States that routinely check their residents for lead levels.

In a pilot study conducted in 1979 by the Court Clinic Research Foundation in Chicago, 29 hardened adult offenders were evaluated for their physiologic mineral and toxic metal levels. Twenty seven out of 29 offenders were found to have elevated levels of lead, in addition to high aluminum and tin and deficient levels of iron.[50]

Screening For Lead

Calibrating a person's lead level is vital to eliminating lead as a factor affecting behavior.

Determination of lead poisoning and sub-toxic exposure has traditionally been done through blood tests. An enzyme, delta-aminolevulinic acid dehydratase (ALA), essential to the functioning of red blood cells, is inhibited whenever any level of lead exposure occurs. Unfortunately, blood lead does not correlate with bone, muscle, fat, organ or hair tissue lead levels. This older method for testing body burdens of lead is gradually being replaced by two new techniques I have found most helpful in determining heavy metal concentrations, *hematofluorometry* and *hair trace mineral analysis*.

Hematofluorometry

In 1977, Drs. A.A. Lamola and W.E. Blumberg at Bell Laboratories, developed the hematofluorometer, a simple portable device, which can test lead levels in seconds from a single drop of blood placed on a microscope slide. [51-52] False positive results can occur in patients with iron deficiency anemia. Unconfirmed reports suggest that persons who consume large quantities of salicylates, such as aspirin, also can cause false positive readings. Ideal for mass screenings, the hematofluorometer is being increasingly used since reliability and tissue correlation studies have been reported.[53-56]

The hematofluorometer was first demonstrated to me by Dr. Thomas Stone, a psychiatrist in Des Plaines, Illinois. Using an Autolet[57] to painlessly prick my finger, he placed the drop of blood on a slide which he inserted into the hematofluorometer. A second later the device had calibrated my lead level.

Clearly, the hematofluorometer[58] is simple to operate and provides a quick lead level calibration. It should occasionally be correlated with other extraction techniques and has to be calibrated differently for children and adults. Simple to operate, providing quick results, and inexpensive, the hematofluorometer could be a worthwhile screening tool in the hands of trained correctional personnel.

Hair Analysis

Hair trace mineral analysis, another technique receiving increasing acceptance, determines the levels of normal minerals, such as iron and zinc, and toxic elements, such as lead and mercury, in the hair.

Hair is a cellular product excreted by the body. By analyzing hair, a trained health professional gains valuable data about the metabolic balance of a patient. In a 1977 study in the *American Journal of Clinical Nutrition,* hair was shown reflective of a subject's total nutritional environment,[59] including absorption of protein, carbohydrate, fat, vitamins and minerals. Whereas blood values inform the health professional what is in the blood, hair analysis provides a record of how the body uses, stores and disposes of elements.

The hair sample is cut from the back of the head, near the nape of the neck. About a gram (equivalent to two tablespoons of hair) is clipped from the one inch closest to the scalp. If head hair is not available, pubic hair is the next best choice. Even fingernail clippings, if abundantly available, can be similarly analyzed. Taking a hair sample is simple and causes little discomfort. The sample can even be stored for weeks, unlike blood which is biologically unstable.

Besides evaluating the levels of toxic elements in the body, hair analysis can also provide levels for:

calcium	chromium	selenium
magnesium	lithium	cobalt
sodium	nickel	molybdenum
potassium	phosphorous	beryllium
iron	copper	silicon
zinc	manganese	vanadium
	tin	

Knowing the levels and ratios of these elements in the body can provide a valuable adjunctive tool to understanding the total body chemistry of a patient. The significance of this diagnostic approach is reported in numerous studies[60-73] and books [74-79] The reliability of this method has been reported in over 160 published studies. The most concise and thorough papers on this diagnostic technique have been written by Thomas Maugh in *Science*[80] and Dr. Jeffrey Bland in *The Use of the Hair Trace Mineral Analysis in the Clinical Laboratory.*[81]

Using Hair Analysis In Casework

The usefulness of hair analysis can be illustrated by several case histories.

Tim, nine years old, a highly excitable boy whose school work was failing, displayed little self-control in school or at home. He was referred by his school social worker after assaulting other students in the playground. Counseling and parent effectiveness training for Tim's parents proved of little value. The schools were at their wit's end because of his assaultive behavior. The mother refused the school's option that he be placed on medication.

I routinely do a hair analysis on any client I work with, especially, when, as in Tim's case, their behavior can not be rationally explained. His hair analysis is illustrated in Figure 3. [This is only a portion of the hair analysis report received from Mineralab, Inc., Hayward, California and Acton, Massachusetts. The ratios and other information are not shown.] As can be seen from the hair analysis data, Tim's copper, aluminum and arsenic levels are too high. He is borderline on magnesium and zinc, and deficient in sodium, potassium, manganese, nickel, and chromium. Under a physician's guidance, Tim was provided with zinc sulfate supplements to bring his high copper down, since they are antagonists. After three weeks, Tim's mother reported that he had voluntarily cleaned his room for the very first time. He became less moody and less aggressive. His school work markedly improved, confirmed by his school social worker and teacher, with improved penmanship and learning skills.

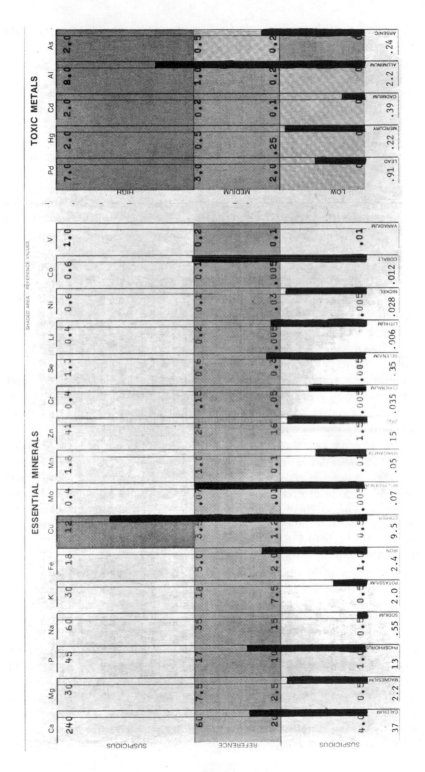

43   Fig. 3

Tim continued to improve after being placed on an additive free diet with no sugar. Because of this dietary treatment, the likelihood of Tim becoming a juvenile delinquent has distinctly lessened.

Another case, Peter, a 14 year old obese youth, was referred to me for his unprovoked aggressive behavior in school. He was on the verge of being expelled by the school district. When he became angry his teachers and classmates watched him at a distance for fear he might attack them. At 210 pounds he presented a formidable presence. His mother informed me that he ate constantly. A computer analysis of his diet revealed that he consumed in excess of 9,700 calories a day! This amount of calories is 50 percent higher than nutrition scientists have estimated is required by an active soldier during manuevers in the Arctic region in mid-winter. Peter's hair analysis revealed, ironically, a nutritionally impoverished boy; with deficient levels of calcium, magnesium, sodium, potassium, copper, manganese, zinc, lithium, and nickel. His aluminum level was elevated. A consulting physician felt he suffered from over-consumption malnutrition due to malabsorption. This theory seemed especially plausible after learning that Peter consumed a minimum of 9 gallons of milk a week. Yet his calcium and magnesium levels were low. He was scheduled for a Heidelberg Gastric Test[82-85] to measure his gastric acid secretion for different foods to determine if he does have a malabsorption problem at the time this book went to press. It seems highly likely that if Peter can get the nutrients he needs into his cells and eat a more moderate amount of food his aggression will diminish.

Arnold, age 26, was referred to us for wife beating. Hair Analysis revealed elevated levels of sodium, potassium, iron, and *four* toxic metals, lead, mercury, cadmium, and aluminum. He was recommended for chelation therapy but refused and left the state with his wife. Efforts to encourage him to receive treatment in his new home state failed. This points out the difficulty in working with some clients. It is only hoped that Arnold will get the help he needs before he seriously harms his wife.

The need to screen for lead and many other elements as a preventive measure in the field of criminology is given importance by a 1940's study of 20 children with "mild" lead poisoning, evaluated over many years, which revealed that only one remained unaffected by delayed behavioral or mental disturbance.[86] The 19 children affected by lead poisoning eventually suffered from such problems as poor handwriting; constant mood swings; dyslexia; poor learning skills; hyperaggressiveness; pyromania; and, *delinquency.*

Data from a 1975-79 study by the New Jersey Childhood Lead Poisoning Program in *Archives of Environmental Health* states:

"Our failure as a society to take the necessary steps results not only in supervision of many cases of lead poisoning but also in the possibility that a far greater number of children are being mentally damaged by subtle, clinically inapparent lead intoxication. [87-88]
It seems entirely possible that the educational failure and *anti-social behavior* that permeate deprived urban areas could be in part a consequence of unrecognized lead-induced brain damage.[89]"

It is highly recommended that the reader secure a copy of *A Clinician's Guide To Toxic Metals: Sources, Occupational Exposures, Signs and Symptoms.*[90] This book contains concise information on other toxic metals that have no known biologic role, as well as, others thought to be essential at lower concentrations, but toxic at high levels (nickel, arsenic, and copper). All these metals are known to cause changes in behavior and have been reported in excessive amounts in juvenile delinquents and adult offenders.

Another problem of modern times are food additives, which is the subject of the next chapter.

References

1. National Academy of Sciences. Toxicants Occurring Naturally in Foods. 1972, p. 61.
2. TUCKER, Anthony, The Toxic Metals. Earth Island Ltd., London, 1972. See, also: GERRAS, Charles (ed.) The Complete Book of Minerals for Health. Rodale Press, 1977, p. 341-342.
3. KIRSCHMAN, John (ed.) Nutrition Almanac: Revised Edition. McGraw-Hill Book Company; New York, 1979, p. 72.
4. Survey of Lead In Food, First Supplementary Report, 1975 (Her Majesty's Stationery Office; London, England).
5. Ibid.
6. BRYCE-SMITH', Derek, MATTHEWS, John and STEPHENS, Robert, Mental Health Effects of Lead on Children. Ambio. 7(5-6): 200, 1978.
7. TUCKER, Anthony, ibid. See, also: WELLS, A.C. et al. Inhaled Particles IV. In: Walton, W.H. (ed.) Pergamon Press, Oxford, England, 1977, p. 175.
8. ZIEGLER, E.E. et al, Pediatric Research. 12(29), 1978. Also, see: ADEBONOJO, F.O. and STRABS, R. Clinical pediatrics. 13(310), 1974.
9. BARLTROP, D. and STREHLOW, S.H. The Absorption of Lead by Children. Report to the International lead Zinc Research Organization, LH 228, June, 1977.
10. JOSELOW, M. et al. Environmental contrasts: Blood lead levels of children in Honolulu and Newark. J. Environ Health. 37:10-12, 1974.
11. DAVID, O. et al. Lead and hyperactivity - behavioral response to chelation: a pilot study. Amer. J. Psychiatry. 133:1155-1158, 1976.
12. CHAIKLIN, H. et al. Recurrence of lead poisoning in children. Social Work. 19:196-200, 1974.
13. U. S. Public Health Service, Center for Disease Control. Increased Lead Absorption and Lead Poisoning in Children. 1975.
14. CHAIKLIN, Harris. The Treadmill of Lead. Amer. J. Orthopsychiat. 49(4): 571-573, 1979.
15. Personnel Communication, 1977.
16. PIHL, R.O. and PARKES, M. Hair Element Content in Learning Disabled Children. Science. 198: 204-206, 1977.
17. NEEDLEMAN, Herbert L., et al. Deficits in Psychologic and Classroom Performance of Children with Elevated Dentine Lead Levels. New England J Med. 300: 689-695, March 29, 1979.
18. NEEDLEMAN, Herbert L. DAVIDSON, I., SEWELL, E.M., et al. Subclinical Lead Exposure in Philadelphia School Children: Identification by Dentine Lead Analysis. New Eng J Med. 290: 245-248, 1974.
19. NEEDLEMAN, Herbert L., et al. Ibid, p. 694.
20. de la BURDE, B. and CHOATE, M.S. Early Asymptomatic Lead Exposure and Development at School Age. J Pediatrics. 87: 638-664, 1975.
21. BYERS, R.K. and LOUD, E.E. Late Effects of Lead Poisoning on Mental Development. Am J Disabled Children. 66: 471-494, 1943.
22. DAVID, O., CLART, J. and VOELLER, K. Lead and Hyperactivity. The Lancet. 2: 900-903, 1972.
23. BRYCE-SMITH, Derek and WALDRON, H.A. Lead, Behaviour and Criminality. The Ecologist. 4(10); 367, December, 1974. (England)
24. BRYCE-SMITH, Derek and WALDRON, H.A. ibid.
25. NEEDLEMAN, Herbert L. et al, ibid, p. 694.
26. New York City Department of Health, Bureau of Lead Poisoning Control. The New York City Lead Poisoning Program: Achievements and Needs. April 22, 1977, p. 2.

27. BERMAN, A. Neurological Dysfunction In Juvenile Delinquents: Implications for Early Intervention. Child Care Quarterly. 1(4): 264-271, 1972.
28. JACOBSEN, F. The Juvenile Court Judge and Learning Disabilities. Law Enforcement Assistance Administration (monograph). LEAA 76-JN-99-0016, 1976.
29. BRODER, P.K. The Relationship Between Self-reported Juvenile Delinquency and Learning Disabilities: A Preliminary Look At The Data. National College of Juvenile and Family Court Judges, Reno, Nevada, July, 1977.
30. SAWICKI, Donna and SCHAEFFER, Beatrix, An Affirmative Approach to the LD/JD Link. Juvenile & Family Court Judges, Reno, Nevada, July, 1977.
31. Personal Communications, 1979.
32. FOGEL, Max L. Warning: Auto Fumes May Lower Your Kid's IQ. Psychology Today. 13(8): 108, January, 1980.
33. BALANDIER, Georges, Daily Life in the Kingdom of the Kongo: From the Sixteenth to Eighteenth Century. Meridian Books; New York, 1968, p. 113.
34. GORDON, Gary F. Lead Toxicity. American Acad. Med. Preventics, Sacramento, California, 1976, p. 8.
35. CORWIN, Alsoph H. Chelation: A Lecture Demonstration. Presentation at the 13th Advanced Seminar of the Society for Clinical Ecology, San Digeo, California, October 28, 1979.
36. PFEIFFER, Carl C. Mental and Elemental Nutrients. Keats Publishing; New Canaan, Conn., 1975, p. 131-132.
37. KIRSCHMAN, John D., ibid, p. 72.
38. LEDERER, L.G. and BING, F.C. Effect of Calcium and Phosphorous on Retention of Lead by Growing Organism. JAMA. 114: 2457, 1940.
39. SHIELDS, J.B. and MITCHELL, H.H. The Effect of Calcium and Phosphorous on the Metabolism of Lead. J. Nutrition. 21: 541, 1941.
40. SIX, K.M. and GOYER, R.A. Experimental Enhancement of Lead Toxicity by Low Dietary Calcium. J Lab Clin Med. 76: 933, 1970.
41. QUARTERMAN, J., et al. The Influence of Dietary Calcium and Phosphate on Lead Metabolism. Trace Substances in Environmental Health: VII. IN: HEMPHILL, Delbert D. (ed.), University of Missouri Press, 1973, p. 347.
42. Personal Communication, 1979.
43. NIKLOWITZ, W.J. and YEAGER, D.W. Interference of Pb with Essential Brain Tissue Cu, Fe, and Zn as Main Determinant in Experimental Tetraethyl lead Encephalopathy. Life Sciences. 13: 897-905, 1973.
44. TUCKER, Anthony, The Toxic Metals. Earth Island Ltd., London, 1972.
45. PFEIFFER, Carl C. Zinc and Other Micro-Nutrients. Pivot Original Health Book, New York, 1978, p. 163.
46. GORDON, Gary F. ibid, p. 2, and personal communication, 1979.
47. GRIGGS, R.C. SUNSHINE, I., NEWILL, V.A., NEWTON, B.W., BUCHANAN, S., AND RASCH, C.A. Environmental Factors in Childhood Lead Poisoning. JAMA. 187:703, 1964.
48. SCHUCKER, G.W., VAIL, E.H., KELLEY, E.B. and KAPLAN, E. Prevention of Lead Paint Poisoning Among Baltimore Children. Public Health Report. 80: 969, Washington, D.C., 1965.
49. Full Circle School is located in Bolinas, California (near San Francisco). The School works with wards of the California Youth Authority.
50. Personal communication, Jerry Knight, 1979.
51. BLUMBERG, W.E., EISINGER, J., LAMOLA, A.A. and ZUCKERMAN, D.M. Zinc Protoporphyrin Level In Blood Determined By A Portable Hematofluorometer: A Screening Device for Lead Poisoning. J. Laboratory & Clinical Med. 89(4): 712-723, 1977.

52. BLUMBERG, W.E. EISINGER, J., LAMOLA, A.A. and ZUCKERMAN, D.M. The Hematofluorometer. J Clinc Chem. 23(2): 270-274, 1977.
53. LAMOLA, A.A., EISINGER, J. BLUMBERG, W.E. KOVETANI, T. and B.F. Quantitative Determination of Erthrocyte Zinc Protoporphyrin. J. Lab Clin Med. 89(4): 881-890, 1977.
54. EISINGER, J. Biochemistry and Measurement of Environmental Lead Intoxication. Q Reviews Biophysics. 2(4): 439-466, 1978.
55. EISINGER, J. and BLUMBERG, W.E. Zinc Protoporphyrin In Blood as a Biological Indicator of Chronic Lead Intoxication. J Environ Pathology Toxicology. 1: 897-910, 1978.
56. EISINGER, J. and FLORES, J. Front-face Fluorometry of Liquid Samples. Analytical Biochemistry. 94: 15-21, 1979.
57. The Autolet is available from Ulster Scientific, PO Box 902, Highland, N.Y. 12528.
58. The Hematofluorometer is available from AVIA Associates, P. O. Box 994, Lakewood, N.J. 08701.
59. GERSHOFF, S. MCGANDY, R., et al. Trace Minerals in Human and Rat Hair. Am J Clin Nutr. 30: 868, 1977.
60. HOPPS, H. The Biologic Bases for Using Hair and Nail for Analyses of Trace Elements. Trace Substances in Environmental Health: VIII. University of Missouri, 1974, pp. 59-73.
61. GORDUS, A. Factors Affecting the Trace-Metal Content of Human Hair. J Radio-analytical Chem. 15: 229-243, 1973.
62. McKENZIE, J. Alteration of the Zince and Copper Concentration of Hair. Am J Clin Nutr. 31: 470-476, 1978.
63. RUDOLPH, C. Trace Element Patterning in Degenerative Diseases. J Int Acad Prev Med. 4(1), July, 1977.
64. CHATTOPADHYAH, A ROBERTS, T. and JERVISE, R. Scalp Hair as a Monitor of Community Exposure to lead. Archives Environ Health. 32(5): 226-236, Sept/Oct, 1977.
65. RABINOWITZ, M., WETHERILL, G. and KOPPLE, J. Delayed Appearance of Tracer Lead in Facial Hair. Archives Environ Health. 31(4): 220-223, 1976.
66. YAMAGUCHI, S., et al. A Background of Geographical Pathology on Mercury in the East Pacific Area. J Occupational Med. 19(7): 502-504, July, 1977.
67. Lin, H.J. et al. Zinc Levels in Serum, Hair, and Tumors from Patients with Esophageal Cancer. Nutr Reports Int. 15(6): 635-641, 1977.
68. HAMBRIDGE, K. et al. Low Levels of Zinc in Hair, Anorexia, Poor Growth, and Hypogeusia in Children. Pedia Res. 6: 868-874, 1972.
69. JACOB, R. KLEVAY, L. and LOGAN, G. Hair as a Biopsy Material Versus Hair as a Chronic Lead Poisoning. New Eng J Med. 276: 949, 1967, March, 1978.
70. GREGER, J., et al. Nutritional Status of Adolescent Girls in regard to Zinc, Copper, and Iron. Am J Clin Nutr. 31: 269-275, February, 1978.
71. SANER, G. and GURSON, C. Hair Chromium Concentration in Newborns and their Mothers. Nutr Reprts Int. 14(2): 155-164, 1976.
72. KOPITO, L. and SHWACHMAN, H. Spectroscopic Analysis of Tissues from Patients with Cystic Fibrosis and Controls. Nature. 202: 501, 1964.
73. KOPITO, L. BYERS, R.K., and SHWACHMAN, H. Lead in Hair of Children with Chronic lead Poisoning. New Eng J Med. 276: 949, 1967.
74. PRASAD, ANANDA. Trace Elements in Human Health and Disease: I, II. Academic Press, New York, 1976.
75. UNDERWOOD, E. Trace Elements in Human and Animal Nutrition. Academic Press, New York, 1977.
76. SCHROEDER, Henry. The Poisons Around Us. Indiana Univ. Press, 1974.

77. SCHROEDER, Henry. Trace Elements and Ma. Devin-Adair; Old Greenwich, Conn., 1978.
78. PFEIFFER, Carl. Zinc and Other Micro-Nutrients. Keats Publishing; New Canaan, Conn., 1978.
79. PFEIFFER, Carl. Mental and Elemental Nutrients. Keats Publishing; New Canaan, Conn., 1975.
80. MAUGH, Thomas Hair: A Diagnostic Tool to Complement Blood, Serum and urine. Science. 202: 1271, 1978.
81. BLAND, Jeffrey Hair Tissue Mineral Analysis: An Emergent Diagnostic Technique. Bellevue-Redmond Laboratories, Washington, 1979.
82. The Heidelberg Gastric Test can determine achlorhydria (low acid in the stomach), low alkalinity in the duodenum, and pancreatic insufficiency, all factors in malabsorption or maldigestion of foods.
83. YARBROUGH, Dabney R., McALHANY, Joseph C., COOPER, Norman and WELDNER, Michael G. Evaluation of the Heidelberg pH Capsule Method of Tubeless Gastric Analysis. Am J Surgery. 117(2): 185-192, 1969.
84. NOLLER, H.G. The Use of a Radiotransmitter Capsule for the Measurement of Gastric pH. German Medical Monthly. 6:3, 1961.
85. The Heidelberg pH method of tubeless gastric analysis is available as the Gastrogram machine from Electro-Medical Devices, Inc., Atlanta, Ga. 30360.
86. BYERS, R.K. and LORD F.E. Late Effects of lead Poisoning on Mental Development. Am J Disabled Children. 66: 471, 1943.
87. BROWDER, A.A., JOSELOW, M.M. and LOURIA, D.B. The Problem of Lead Poisoning. Medicine. 52:2, 1973.
88. de la BURDE, C., Jr., Does Asymptomatic lead Exposure In Children Have latent Sequelae? Pedriatrics. 88: 1088-91, 1972.
89. FOSTER, James D., LOURIA, Donald B. and STINSON, Lydia, Influence of Documented Lead Poisoning on Environmental Modification Programs in Newark, New Jersey. Arch Environ Health. Sept/Oct, 1979.
90. A Clinician's Guide to Toxic Metals: Sources, Occupational Exposures, Signs and Symptoms. Mineralab, Inc., 3106 Diablo Ave., Hayward, Ca. 94545, 1979. Also discusses aluminum, arsenic, cadmium, copper, mercury, and nickel.

Bibliography

BLAND, Jeffrey, Hair Tissue Mineral Analysis: An Emergent Diagnostic Technique. Bellevue-Redmond Medical Laboratories, Washington, 1979.
GORDON, Gary, Lead Toxicity (pamphlet). American Academy of Medical Preventics, 2811 L Street, Sacramento, California 95816, 1977.
LESSER, Michael, Nutrition and Vitamin Therapy (Chapter Eight; Detecting and Avoiding The Toxic Metals.) Grove Press; New York, 1980.
OEHME, Frederick W. (ed.) Toxicity of Heavy Metals In The Environment: Part 1. Marcel Decker, Inc.; New York, 1978.
PFEIFFER, Carl, Mental and Elemental Nutrients. Keats Publishing; New Canaan, Conn., 1975.
PFEIFFER, Carl, Zinc and other Micronutrients. Keats Publishing; New Canaan, Conn., 1978.
SCHROEDER, henry, The Poisons Around Us. Indiana Univ. Press, 1974.
SCHROEDER, Henry, Trace Elements and Man. Devin-Adair; Old Greenwich, Conn., 1978.
Toxic Metals: Sources, Occupational Exposures, Signs and Symptoms (A Clinician's Guide). Mineralab, Inc. 3106 Diablo Ave., Hayward, California 94545, 1979.
TUCKER, Anthony, The Toxic Metals. Earth Island, Ltd.; London, 1972.
UNDERWOOD, E. Trace Elements in Human and Animal Nutrition. Academic Press; New York, 1977.
WILLIAMS, Roger J. and KALITA, Dwight K. A Physician's Handbook on Orthomolecular Medicine. Pergamon Press; New York, 1977.

IV

FOOD ADDITIVES, BEHAVIOR AND DELINQUENCY

A school teacher writes describing one of her elementary grade students. Her description of his behavior is remarkably like that of juvenile offenders of a similar age. Her letter reads:

"Jay, a second grader (eight years old), is at times crabby and paranoid (thinks the other kids and teacher are picking on him). He cannot finish his work or concentrate on days when he is under the influence of junk food. His face is pale and sunken, his eyes glassy, with dark circles under them. He cries easily, can't get organized, loses things and blames others.

His school work is definitely affected. His handwriting on bad days is an illegible scrawl, though on good days it is well formed.

At home he has difficulty getting up in the morning, doesn't get along with anyone and blames his mother for not letting him eat anything and everything...Jay is a normal happy child when eating the right things. He is impossible when off the diet."

Hyperactivity is an increasingly severe problem. During the last decade, over a hundred million Ritalin® tablets were prescribed in the United States to help control an estimated 300,000 hyperkinetic children. During this same period, the number of food additives in our diet has steadily increased.

In 1948, Dr. Stephen Lockey, a Lancaster, Pennsylvania, allergist, reported the first case of sensitivity to artificial food colors,[1] reporting that many of his patients' behavior improved when they eliminated food dyes from their diets.

In 1972, Dr. Ben Feingold reported to the meeting of the American Medical Association that artificial flavorings and colorings may be the cause of learning disability and hyperactive behavior in perhaps half the children so labeled.

Dr. Feingold, author of *Why Your Child Is Hyperactive*[2], found that, for every girl reacting to the additives, nine boys were found to be sensitive.[3] This is close to the proportion of boys to girls reported to be delinquent in the United States. [4-5]

Dr. Feingold classified 2,764 food additives in 1967 as follows:[2]

Classification of Intentional Food Additives

Preservatives	33
Antioxidants	28
Sequestrants (chelating agents, metal scavangers, emulsifiers, stabilizers)	45
Surface active agents	111
Stabilizers and thickeners	39
Bleaching and maturing agents	24
Buffers, acids, alkalies	60
Food colors	34
Non-nutritive and special dietary sweeteners	4
Nutritive supplements	117
Flavorings, natural	502
Flavorings, synthetic	1,610
Miscellaneous (yeast foods, texturizers, firming agents, binders, anti-caking agents, enzymes)	157

By 1980, according to the Center for Science in the Public Interest, Washington, D.C., this list has grown considerably longer.[3 8 7]

In 1975, the Interagency Collaborative Group on Hyperkinesis of the U.S. Department of Health, Education and Welfare and the National Advisory Committee of the Nutrition Foundation concluded that no acceptable evidence existed to support the claims of a link between hyperactivity and food additives. [6-7] They reached this conclusion despite the reports of Feingold[8] and the work of Dr. B.H. Ershoff on the effects of additives on laboratory rats. Feeding rats a typical Western diet high in carbohydrates and low in fiber, rather than the more nutritious standard diet chow, the toxic and behavioral effects of additives were clearly observable.[9]

The following year, three other physicians published results confirming Dr. Feingold's contentions. [10-12] But other researchers published studies which showed inconsistent results. [13-15]

The Dosage of Additives Is Crucial

In any investigation of the pharmacological effect of a substance on behavior, the dosage of the substance is obviously crucial. The challenge dosage of food color in the negative studies was 26 milligrams, given to the hyperactive children by putting 13 milligrams (mg) of a dye in each cookie. The cookies were named after the Nutrition Foundation which made the recommendation to use only 26 mg of food dye in the experiments. The subjects were usually given one cookie in the morning and one in the early afternoon; a total of 26 mg of additives per day. These dosage levels produced, at most, only a minimal worsening of behavior among some subjects.

But two Toronto, Canada physicians, James M. Swanson and Marcel Kinsbourne, determined in 1979 that the dosage level of food dyes used in the Nutrition Foundation cookies had been too small. The Nutrition Foundation estimated the average daily consumption of artificial dyes by dividing the tons of artificial food colors manufactured each year by the U.S. population, then dividing by 365 days, to arrive at the daily dosage (26 mg per day). But as Dr. Swanson and Kinsbourne stated, "This method assumes that people of all ages consume the same amount of color, which may be an unreasonable assumption...it is likely that children consume more food with a high concentration of artificial color than adults."[16]

The doctors requested the aid of the Biochemical Toxicology Branch of the Food and Drug Administration (FDA). The FDA indicated that the Nutrition Foundation's estimates were far too low. Based on a recent survey of the diets of 5,000 children aged six to ten, the average daily intake of food dyes was closer to 75 mg per day. The FDA found that 10 percent of U.S. children were getting as much as 150 mg of artificial color a day, while a few consumed over 300 mg per day. This helped explain the previous inconsistencies of other studies.

Dr. Feingold maintains that other researchers have failed to consider the synergistic effects of colors, salicylates, flavorings, and other additives working together in the body.

Using doses of artificial colors between 100 and 150 mg, Swanson and Kinsbourne tested the reactions of the known hyperkinetic behavior and artificial food colors because the they gave the children capsules rather than the cookies used in the former studies. While no difference was observed after administration of the 100 mg challenge at 30 minutes, a significant difference in performance (i.e., concentration, distractibility, etc.) was observed at the one and one-half to three-hour intervals. This difference was even more evident when 150 mg challenges were administered. Previous studies had failed to show a link between the hyperkinetic behavior and artificial food colors because the quantity of food color given the children had been too small. Only after challenged with 100 to 150 mg capsules did the children clearly respond.

A National Institutes of Health (NIH) study supported Dr. Feingold's position that the effect of additives is not necessarily an allergic reaction but the pharmacologic effect of salicylates and certain classes of food dyes.[17] The NIH research demonstrated that extremely small concentrations of erythrosine (Red Dye No. 3) inhibited the uptake of dopamine by rat brain tissue. Disturbances in dopamine uptake have been implicated in minimal brain dysfunction and other behavioral disorders. [18-19] The NIH study felt there was no question that enough dye is present in foods such as soft drinks, licorice, and candies to produce an effect. Yet no one knows how much of the dye is absorbed by the intestine, enters the blood stream, and eventually passes through the blood brain barrier to affect behavior. Whether the dye reaches the brain and in what amounts may account for the varied reactions to the dye among individuals.

It may be years before the arguments over Dr. Feingold's hypothesis is proven right or wrong. In the meantime, tens of thousands of parents in over ten countries remain unshaken in their belief that the Feingold Diet works. Few parents really care to know why it works, if it helps.

The Diet of a Typical Case:

Dr. Clifford E. Simonsen and I studied the diets of chronic juvenile delinquents and found numerous examples of the consumption of considerable quantities of food additives, as illustrated by the following case:

Male:	14 years, 2 months
Grade:	7
NBI Score:	91
Charge:	Vandalism
Previous Offenses:	2 prior 2nd-degree burglaries in 2 years
Breakfast:	5 cups Sugar Smacks with ½ teaspoon added sugar
	1 glazed white donut
	2 glasses of milk (20 ounces)
Snacks:	1 foot-long rope of red licorice
	3 six inch beef jerky sticks
Lunch:	2 hamburgers
	French fries
	2 foot-long ropes of red licorice
	Small serving of green beans
	Little or no salad

                              2 slices of white bread with no butter
                              3, 8-ounce cartons of chocolate milk

P.M. Snack: Apple and small glass of water

Dinner: Peanut butter/jelly sandwich, white bread
                                 no butter
                              1 can of Campbell's tomato soup
                              1 10-ounce glass of sweetened Kool-Aid

late Snack: 1 large bowl of ice cream
                              1 Marathon candy bar
                              1 small glass of water

The following symptoms were described by this youth on the Nutrition Behavior Inventory (NBI) as "usual":

--After I fall asleep, I wake up and cannot get back to sleep
--I get headaches
--I have itching or crawling sensations on my skin
--I sigh or yawn during the day
--My stomach or intestines are upset
--I get bruises or black and blue marks easily
--I have nightmares or bad dreams
--I get faint, dizzy or have cold sweats or weak spells
--I nibble between meals when I am hungry
--I get hungry or feel faint if I do not eat often
--I often forget things
--I eat sweet things or drink coffee or tea in the afternoon
--I add sugar to most things I eat or drink
--I am very restless
--I cannot work under pressure
--It is hard to decide things
--I feel depressed
--I constantly worry about things
--I get confused
--I get depressed or feel the blues over nothing
--I blow little things out of proportion and easily lose my temper
--I get fearful
--I feel very nervous
--I am highly emotional
--I cry for no apparent reason

Computer analysis of his diet revealed he was deficient in the B-vitamin folic acid intake and consumed 36 teaspoons of "hidden sugar" a day. He was also *below* the suggested optimum in Vitamin E, Vitamin C, Vitamin B_1, B_2, B_5, B_6, B_{12}, PABA, Biotin, Bioflavinoids and the minerals Selenium and Vanadium. He was found to be *above* the optimum in total calories, fat, refined carbohydrates, protein, sodium and acid ash.

Reviewing this 14-year-old's diet, it becomes evident he is consuming considerable quantities of food colors, artificial flavors, salicylates and preservatives. Based on the conclusions of Drs. Feingold, Swanson, Kinsbourne, and others, this youth might benefit from a diet free of these additives. Unfortunately, over 99 percent of probation departments do not evaluate the diets of their clients to uncover similar patterns of poor nutrition.

How The Feingold Diet Works

In Dr. Feingold's new book, *The Feingold Cookbook for Hyperactive Children* (Random House), [20] two groups of foods are to be eliminated. Group I consists of all foods that contain synthetic (artificial) colors and synthetic (artificial) flavors. Additionally, two antioxidant preservatives, compounds used to keep foods from spoiling, butylated hydroxytoluene (BHT) and butylated hydroxyanisole (BHA), are also eliminated. To determine whether a food or beverage contains these ingredients, read the label. In certain cases, however, these compounds are not listed on the label. For example, BHT or BHA are added to synthetic Vitamin D to prevent it from turning rancid. Later this fat soluble vitamin containing BHT or BHA is added to milk as required by law. Most low fat milk also contains gylcerol monoleate, an artificial butter flavor used as an emulsifier.

Group II foods comprise a number of fruits and vegetables that contain natural salicylates. The following vegetables, fruits and miscellaneous items contain salicylates and should be eliminated:[21]

Almonds	Grapes & raisins
Apples	(wine & wine vinegar)
(also cider & cider vinegar)	Green peppers (also chilies)
Apricots	Nectarines
All berries	Oranges
Cherries	Peaches
Cloves	Plums & prunes
Coffee	Tangerines
Cucumbers	All teas
Pickles	Tomatoes
Currants	Oil of Wintergreen

Dr. Feingold lists a number of common household items which also need to be eliminated in Group II, such as: all mouthwashes; cough drops and lozenges; perfumes; disinfectants, deodorizers and insecticides; and, all toothpastes and toothpowders. For a comprehensive listing, the reader is urged to read his book.

Tehama County Probation Program

In 1977, Robert G. Lucas, Chief Probation Officer, Tehama County Probation Department (California), noticing that children held at the Tehama County Juvenile Hall became increasingly hyperactive and aberrant, and aware of Feingold's work, decided to change the eating habits of children in his institution.[22]

Quantities of on-hand food had to be used before instituting the new dietary regime. As foods were consumed, they were either not reordered or substitutions were provided.

Foods Eliminated	Substitution
Sugar (granulated or powdered)	Honey
Syrup	Honey
Sugar-coated cereals	Plain cereals
Ham	Other meats
Jello desserts	Knox gelatin with fruit chunks & juices
Packaged foods	Foods prepared on grounds
Kool-Aid, coffee, tea, soda pop	Milk, water, fruit juice (unsweetened/natural)
Bread with preservatives	Bread without preservatives
Jelly & fruit preserves	Honey & fresh fruit
Flavor enhancers	None
Syrup-packed fruits	Water-packed fruits
Chocolate	Carob
Foods containing dyes	Foods without dyes
Candy	Fruit
Animal fat shortening	Vegetable shortening
White flour	Whole wheat flour

In the kitchen, food preparation personnel learned to adjust recipes, menus and purchasing habits. When told of the changes, the staff generally received the news well, although a few of the old guard grumbled. Within a few months, nearly complete elimination of foods with traces of dyes and preservatives had been accomplished.

Lucas describes the case of Neil as an example of his program's success. Neil, hyperactive, belligerent, irritable; hadn't been able to stay out of detention for longer than three months at a time. After two weeks on the improved diet, his "mile a minute" speech slowed to an understandable calm voice. Previously an insomniac, he now slept soundly and became noticeably less irritable. Before the end of his detention, others in the center had noticed his improvement. Although he initially resented the elimination of soda, sugar and candy, he adjusted to the loss, once he was able to recognize that he had changed.

The most striking changes have occured with the delinquent children in the long-term treatment programs. These children are able to notice a difference in the way they feel when they are on a pass and consume even one can of soda pop or eat a single candy bar. Through counseling and parental support, some treatment program graduates have been able to maintain their diet change after release. Teachers seeing these children upon return, remark on how much more stable and less irritable they are.

Juvenile Hall teachers report reduced hyperactivity, less misbehavior and longer attention spans in the classroom. Bedtime, which had always been a time for procrastination, squabbles and much "game playing" has become remarkably quiet. Children now go to bed early. More youths, once in bed, quickly fall asleep and sleep soundly through the night.

At first, the Chief felt the institutional food budget would increase due to the use of more fresh fruits and juices, honey and foods without dyes and preservatives. After one year of operation, however, it was determined that the Tehama County Probation Department had experienced a *14-percent reduction* in the cost of food.

In summary, Chief Lucas wrote to his local newspaper, stating the following:

"Children, staff, school teachers and parents all report less hyperactivity in youngsters who participate in the program. Although diet control and nutrition awareness are not proposed as a panacea for deviant behavior, the true long-term effect is not known. In the past two years a remarkable difference has been observed in the behavior of inmates in the Tehama County Juvenile Hall. Additonally, children are receiving a more nutritionally sound diet and are learning to recognize how their feelings change with diet modification."[23]

Similar improvements in diet were made in 1979 by Richard Brazil, Superintendent of Juvenile Hall, Humboldt County, California. Cooperating with von Humboldt High School, all detainees are educated on proper food habits and nutritionally beneficial foods to eat, according to Chief Probation Officer E. Alan Campbell.

What Other Countries Have Done

It might seem that the incidence of hyperactivity would be similar in all industrialized countries due to the strain of modern life. However, in Western Europe the problem of hyperkinesis is much rarer than in the United States. In England, for example, hyperactivity is reported in only one of every 2,000 children as compared to the United States where the range is from one in three to one in twenty children.[24]

Perhaps this is because Europeans have been more concerned

over what their children eat. In 1977 for example, Norway banned all artificial food colors in foods or beverages.[25]

In 1977, West Germany became shockingly aware of the effects of food additives on its children and youth. Numerous cases were reported in that year indicating that unruly and hyperkinetic children's behavior were preceded by ingestion of food additives. There were also indications that these same additives produced learning difficulties.[26]

The Case of Marcus:

The parents of Marcus, a youth in West Germany, were able to prevent their son's commitment to a residential facility by following their pharmacist's advice to remove all additives from his diet. The results were slow at first. Eventually, they seemed remarkable. Before they learned which additive caused such gross behavioral changes in their son, they described their experiences with him:

"At school...during recess he started fights without provocation. When teachers said to stop or tried to hold him down, he would assault them. At home he kicked in doors, threw toys and furniture at us or hit his two-year-old sister, Claudia.

"The more aggressive he became, the more nervous and helpless we felt. If I punished him physically, he would hit us right back. While we tried to talk to him, he deliberately turned away from us. We began to fear every phone call from the school authorities. They were complaining about Marcus. This even led to arguments between me and my husband. He thought I was too soft on Marcus. The school was about to refer him to the authorities when we learned about the diet. We were very skeptical at first, but felt things could not be worse. On a corrective diet, Marcus began to improve for the first time in years."

What a relief it must have been for those parents!

As a result of the experience of Marcus' parents and others, the West German Ministry of Health commissioned a study in the spring of 1978 to determine if certain additives in German food was responsible for children's erratic and unruly behavior. The German Health Minister, Dr. Ekhard Dietrich, commissioned Drs. Brigitta Roy-Feiler and Thomas Starzinski, University Clinic in Mainz, to set up a double-blind controlled study of hyperkinetic and behaviorally disordered children. Their preliminary results were so significant that the director of the German Criminological Society (*Deutschen Kriminologischen Gessellschaft*) supported their further research.[27]
This is in sharp contrast to the lack of interest shown by similar organizations in the United States.

Based on the work of the Mainz University Clinic, the researchers described what happened:

"A ten-year-old boy was asked to draw a simple human figure. This was done right after he received some additive. Neither the child nor the experimenters knew whether he had received the additive or a placebo.

The first drawing was colorful and the figure had all its appendages. Five minutes later, he had lost all interest in the assignment. The doctors tried to get him to continue. He grabbed another sheet of paper and started again. Two minutes later he stopped. The figure's head and legs were missing. The doctors urged him to continue, but he couldn't. He was now incapable of sitting still, concentrating or holding his pencil.

Later, it was learned that this boy, Jens, was one of the subjects who had received the dosage of food additive."

Boys like Jens are usually sent to a counselor or school principal. They are typical of the kind of youth seen in probation departments and courts. They may be suspended, expelled or, to everyone's satisfaction, quit going to school. If you asked a child like Jens, "why don't you do better in school--you have so much potential!", what is he to say? He doesn't understand what is happening.

Phosphates, Behavior and Learning

The West German study reported that the additive found to have an immediate effect of altering a child's behavior was phosphate.

Phosphate is a salt or ester of phosphoric acid. It is used in the food industry to emulsify and improve the consistency of its products. [28-29] Sodium phosphate is in evaporated milk. [30] Phosphorous insecticide residues are often found in salads. [31] Phosphoric acid is used as a flavor in soft drinks, jellies, frozen dairy products, candy, brews and soft cheese products. [32] It is also found naturally in our diet in combination with other elements that break down in the body to simple phosphates. Dietary sources high in phosphorous are red meats, peas, brown rice, beans and nuts. With the addition of phosphates to our food supply, there is clearly too much phosphate in our diet.

A diet low in *added* phosphates is recommended by the University of Mainz Clinic for hyperkinetic, impulsive or learning-impaired children. Their double-blind studies indicate that phosphate-free diets improve the behavior and learning performance of some behaviorally impaired children.

There is a considerable amount of evidence that food additives may affect behavior. Dr. B.A. Shaywitz reported in 1978 that food dyes do clearly impact on rat pup's activity levels and cognitive performance.[33] Further research is needed on the affects of food additives on behavior, particularly, criminal behavior.

I am not recommending the complete elimination of all additives; most additives are well-tolerated by most of us. However, the studies and experiences cited in this chapter do strongly suggest that certain people, especially children, are highly stressed by certain food additives. Apparently a minimum dose is required to overwhelm the body's coping mechanisms. This concept is not new. Over 400 years ago Paracelsus stated:

"All things are poisons, for there is nothing without poisonous qualities. It is only the dose which makes a thing a poison."[34]

One substance overconsumed by millions is alcohol, the subject of the next chapter.

References

1. BUCKLEY, Robert E. Aniline Dye Sensitivity in Hyperactive Children. Hayward, California, August, 1976. (reprint).
2. FEINGOLD, Ben F. Why Your Child Is Hyperactive. Random House; New York, 1975.
3. FEINGOLD, Ben F. Recognition of Food Additives as a Cause of Symptoms of Allergy. Ann Allergy. 26: 309-313, June, 1968.
4. Sourcebook of Criminal Justice Statistics (1976, 1977, 1978). U.S. Dept. of Justice, Law Enforcement Assistance Administration, NCJISS, p. 605.
5. Children in Custody: An Advanced Report on the Juvenile Detention and Correctional Facility of 1974. U.S. Dept. of Justice, LEAA, U.S. Government Printing Office, 1977.
6. KOLOBYE, A.C. Preliminary Findings and Recommendations. U.S. Dept. Health, Education and Welfare, Washington, D.C., 1975.
7. LIPTON, M. Report to the Nutrition Foundation. Nutrition Foundation, New York, 1975. (He was chairman of the National Advisory Committee on Hyperkinesis and Food Additives).
8. FEINGOLD, Ben F. Hyperkinesis and Learning Disabilities Linked to Artificial Food Flavors and Colors. Am J Nursing. 75: 797-803, 1975.
9. ERSHOFF, B.H. Effects of Dietary Carbohydrates on Sodium Cyclamate Toxicity in Rats Fed a Purified, Low Fiber Diet. Proceedings Soc Experimental Biology Med. 154: 65-68, 1977.
10. SALZMAN, T.J. Estimates of Average, 90th Percentile and Maximum Daily Intakes of FD & C Artificial Colors In One Day's Diets Among Two Groups of Children. Memorandum of July 30, 1976, Dept. of Health, Education and Welfare, Food and Drug Administration, Biochemical Toxicology Branch.
11. COOK, P.S. Woodhill, J.M. The Feingold Dietary Treatment of the Hyperkinetic Syndrome. Med J Australia. 2: 85, 1976.
12. BRENNER, A. A Study of the Efficacy of the Feingold Diet on Hyperactive Children. Clinical Pediatrics. 16: 652-656, 1977.
13. CONNERS, C.K. GOYETTE, C.H., SOUTHWICK, D.A. LEES, J.M., and ANDRULONIS, P.A. Food Additives and Hyperkinesis: A Controlled Double-blind Experiment. Pediatrics. 58: 154, 1976.
14. HARLEY, S.P. and MATTHEWS, C.G. Diet and Behavior in Hyperactive Children. Paper presented at the Annual Meeting of the International Neuropsychology Society, Toronto, February, 1976.
15. HARLEY, S.P. and MATTHEWS, C.G. ibid. Harley is at the U. Wisconsin, Dept. Neurology.
16. SWANSON, James M. and KINSBOURNE, Marcel. Artificial Color and Hyperactive Behavior. In: Rehabilitation, Treatment and Management of Learning Disorders, University Park Press (in press).
17. HASTINGS, A.W. In Vitro Experiments Said To Support Hypothesis That Food Dyes Cause Behavioral Disturbances. Med Tribune. 20(32): 5, October 10, 1979.
18. FERNSTROM, John D. How Food Affects Your Brain. Nutrition Action. 6(12): 5-7, December, 1979.
19. HASTINGS, A.W., ibid.
20. FEINGOLD, Ben F. and Helene S. The Feingold Cookbook for Hyperactive Children. Random House; New York, 1979.
21. Ibid, p. 7.
22. Personal communication, 1979. News release by the Red Bluff Daily News, Red Bluff, California, September, 1979.

23. Personal communication, Chief Probation Officer Robert G. Lucas, Red Bluff, California, 1979.
24. DIVOKY, D. Toward a Nation of Sedated Children. Learning. March, 1973, p. 6-13.
25. Letter to the Editor, J Am Med Assoc (JAMA), 239: 1089, 1978.
26. DIETER, Herold, Das Heimliche Gift. Stern. 40: 31-38, September 23, 1978 (West Germany).
27. Nahrungsphoshat als Nurssache for Verhaltungsstorungen und Jugend Kriminalitat-Eim Erfahrungsbericht. Kriminalistik-Verlag. Heidelberg, West Germany, 1978.
28. ELLINGER, R.H. Phosphates as Food Ingredients. CRC Press; Cleveland, Ohio, 1972.
29 FURIA, Thomas E. (ed.) CRC Handbook of Food Additives, 2nd Edition. CRC Press; Cleveland, Ohio, 1972.
30. WINTER, Ruth, A Consumer's Dictionary of Food Additives. Crown Publishing; New York, 1978.
31. NULL, Gary and Steve, Complete Handbook of Nutrition. Robert Speller & Sons; New York, 1972.
32. FURIA, Thomas E. (ed.), ibid.
33. SHAYWITZ, B.A., GOLDENRING, J.R. and WOLL, R.S. Effects of Chronic Administration of Food Colorings on Activity Levels and Cognitive Performance In Normal and Hyperactive Developing Rat Pups. Annals Neurology. 4:196, 1978.
34. Paracelsus, as cited by Sigerist, H.E., in The Great Doctors, Doubleday and Company, New York, 1958.

Bibliography

AYRES, J.C., KRAFT, A.A. SNYDER, H.E. and WALKER, H.W. (eds.) Chemical and Biological Hazards In Food. Iowa State University Press; Ames, Iowa, 1962.

ELLINGER, R.H. Phosphates as Food Ingredients. CRC Press; Cleveland, Ohio, 1972.

FEINGOLD, Ben F. Introduction to Clinical Allergy. Charles C. Thomas; Springfield, Ill., 1973.

FEINGOLD, Ben F. Why Your Child Is Hyperactive. Random House; New York, 1975.

FEINGOLD, Ben F. and Helene. The Feingold Cookbook for Hyperactive Children. Random House; New York, 1979.

FURIA, Thomas E. (ed.) CRC Handbook of Food Additives, 2nd Edition. CRC Press; Cleveland, ohio, 1972.

FURIA, Thomas E. and BELLANCA, Nicolo; Fenaroli's Handbook of Flavor Ingredients, 2nd Edition. CRC Press; Cleveland, Ohio, 1975 (Volume I and II).

GARRISON, Omar V, Dictocrats' Attack on Health Foods and Vitamins. Arco Publishing; New York, 1970.

HALL, Ross Hume, Food for Nought: The Decline In Nutrition. Harper & Row; New York, 1974.

HUNTER, Beatrice Trum, Consumer Beware! Your Food and What's Been Done To It. Simon and Schuster; New York, 1970.

HUNTER, Beatrice Trum, Fact Book on Food Additives and Your Health. Keats Publishing; New Canaan, Conn., 1972.

JACOBSEN, Michael F. Eater's Digest: The Consumer's Factbook of Food Additives (Updated). Anchor Books; Garden City, New York, 1976.

National Academy of Sciences, Evaluating the Safety of Food Chemicals. No. 1859, Washington, D.C., 1970.

RECHCIGL, Miloslav Jr. CRC Handbook Series in Nutrition and Food, Section I, Food Safety, Food Processing and Food Preservation. CRC Press; Cleveland, Ohio, 1978.

SMITH, Lendon H. Improving Your Child's Behavior Chemistry. Prentice-Hall; Englewood Cliffs, New Jersey, 1976.

TURNER, S. James, The Chemical Feast. Grossman; New York, 1970.

WINTER, Ruth, Beware of Food You Eat, 2nd Edition. Signet Books; New York, 1971.

WINTER, Ruth, A Consumer's Dictionary of Food Additives. Crown Publishers; New York, 1978.

Films and Slides

Eat, Drink and Be Wary (film)

Churchill Films
662 N. Robertson Blvd.
Los Angeles, Calif. 90069

V
ALCOHOLISM, ADDICTION AND DIET

Alcoholism and Diet

In the Danish dependency of Greenland, each Greenlander over age 14 consumes an average of 6 gallons of alcohol per year-the highest per capita rate in the world. Greenland police report that 9 out of 10 crimes on the island take place under the influence of alcohol.[1]

It's conservatively estimated that over 10 million Americans drink excessively; endangering their own health and the safety of others. Extremely complex and pervasive, alcoholism impacts on such other major social problems as traffic safety and child abuse. Since 1971, per capita alcohol consumption has been the highest recorded since 1850, averaging 2.6 gallons of absolute ethanol per person 14 years of age and older.

It is estimated by the National Institute of Alcohol Abuse and Alcoholism that between 29 to 40 percent of all deaths from accidents, homicides, and suicides, are indirectly caused by alcohol. Alcohol abuse and alcoholism cost the United States nearly 43 billion dollars in 1975 according to a recent study.[2] The economic costs associated with alcohol related motor vehicle accidents were estimated at over five billion dollars in 1975.[3] Although probably underestimated, a cost of nearly 3 billion dollars has been estimated for violent crimes-homicide, forcible rape, and aggravated assault related to alcohol.[4] No studies have yet determined the cost of property damage from vandalism, arson, burglary, or other crimes caused by persons under the influence of alcohol. It has been estimated that the net cost of alcohol related fires in 1975 was nearly 500 million dollars.

Few readers are ignorant of the nation's problems with juvenile alcoholism. Estimates exceed three million children.[5] From my own experience in working with over 1,000 juvenile offenders, more than half were arrested while intoxicated by alcohol. A 1979 survey of "typical" young drinkers in one East Texas county indicates they take their first drink at age ten and five years thereafter have consumed alcohol on at least eight occassions.[6] Seventy-one percent of the 700 students polled responded that they had taken their first drink before age 12. The National Institute on Alcohol Abuse and Alcoholism (NIAAA) indicates this is typical of most of America's children.

Diet can have a significant impact on preventing alcoholism. While acknowledging the importance of genetics, the eminent biochemist, Dr. Roger J. Williams, maintains that "no one who follows good nutritional practices will ever become an alcoholic."[7]

In 1973, a research team began a study of 200 alcoholics, aged 13 to 82.[8] Ninety-seven percent showed low blood sugar or hypoglycemia. Remembering that hypoglycemia might better be defined as nutritionally induced chronic endocrinopathy, this is most significant. Among a control population, only 18 percent had hypoglycemia. If there had been no organic damage, the alcoholics' hypoglycemia disappeared once their diet was corrected. This suggests their hypoglycemia should be classified as dietary induced. If they did not remain on their diets and abstain from drinking they reverted to their former hypoglycemic state. The study also revealed that coffee and spices increased the alcoholic's desire for alcohol. This information has apparently not been well circulated to Alcoholics Anonymous (AA) which generally serves copious amounts of coffee and sweets during meetings.

Chronic drinkers have a very inadequate nutritional intake. As the alcoholic's calories come from alcohol rather than food. This results in numerous vitamin and mineral deficiencies, especially of thiamine, iron and Vitamin B_{12}.[9]

Nutrition And Vitamin Therapy Effective For Alcoholism.

Dr. Russell E. Smith reported in 1974 on his work with 507 hardcore alcoholics at Brighton Hospital, Detroit, Michigan, over three-years.[10] During a one-year treatment period each alcoholic received daily spaced dosages of Vitamin B_3 (niacin) in quantities of three to five grams. A follow-up evaluation of treated patients showed a 71 percent recovery rate (sobriety). Dr. Smith commented that niacin therapy along with a hypoglycemic diet resulted in "unprecedented changes among alcoholics who otherwise would have a very poor prognosis." Similar results using niacin therapy and a special diet to control hypoglycemia have been reported by Guest House, a treatment center for rehabilitating priests near Lake Orion, Michigan. They maintain an 82 percent recovery rate over several years of follow-up.

Dr. Abram Hoffer, an internationally recognized authority on nutrition and mental illness[11], investigated the nutritional needs of serious offenders and alcoholics. He found that both groups required large dosages of Vitamin B_3 and B_6.[12] This was confirmed by Dr. R. J. Green, who found that the majority of inmates at the Saskatchewan Penitentiary in Prince Albert, Canada, were suffering from various forms of special vitamin need. One third of the inmates experienced perceptual distortions, believed related to a Vitamin B_6 deficiency.[13]

Employing a similar nutrition and vitamin therapy approach, Dr. David Hawkins, of the North Nassau Mental Health Center in Long Island, one of the nation's largest alcoholism treatment programs, reports a 71 percent success rate. This contrasts with an estimated national alcoholism rehabilitation success rate 25 percent, as reported by NIAAA.

Dr. Hagop S. Mekhjian, Professor of Medicine at Ohio State University, found consistent evidence that the heavy drinker develops nutrient deficiencies.[14] He investigated the effects of drinking on the human intestine of six or seven drinks a day for a period as short as two weeks. This can throw the digestive system literally into *reverse.* The experimental subjects, while fed a balanced nutritious meal, actually had their small intestines pour out fluids that flushed food from the body before it could be absorbed.[15] This prevented the digestive system from absorbing the vitamins, minerals and trace nutrients it required. An alcoholic who does not eat an adequate diet obviously compounds these effects. Once the intestine is in reverse, Mekhjian found that supplemental doses of folic acid could partially correct the disordered digestion. If the person abstained from all alcohol, the abnormalities were completely reversed.

The American Dietetic Association's *Guidelines for Nutritional Care of Alcoholics During Rehabilitation*[16] finds alcoholics are deficient in Vitamins B_1, B_2, B_3, B_6, and folic acid. Dr. Nathan Brody, a physician who treated alcoholics for 23 years, "found very few alcoholics who were not zinc deficient."[17] The likelihood of vitamin and mineral deficiencies in alcoholics must be recognized in any alcoholism rehabilitation program. Coffee consumption should also be examined.

The Department of Health at Loma Linda University in southern California, estimates that every 24 hours American's consume over 400,000,000 cups of coffee containing over 50 tons of caffeine. This amounts to at least 137 billion cups of coffee for the United States in one year. At the 1979 World Congress on Alcoholism Prevention, Dr. Patricia Mutch, head of the nutrition department at Andrews University in Berien Springs, Michigan, reported on animal experiments that led her to conclude that coffee, the drink served so frequently at Alcoholics Anonymous meetings, may actually promote alcoholism if drunk in large quantities (nine cups or more of coffee a day). Dr. Mutch speculates that people may reach for a drink of alcohol to control the shakiness caused by so much coffee.[57]

Heroin, Methadone and Diet

Dr. Nils Bejerot, Research Fellow in Drug Dependence at the Karolinska Institutet in Stockholm, Sweden, points out that addiction functions as an artifically induced drive, both in its psychological and physiological aspects, in which the pleasure and pain principle is the motivating force in both instances.[18] Dr. William H. Philpott, Oklahoma City psychiatrist, agrees that "the personal and/or social factors shaping the introduction to an addictive substance are quite separate facts from the addiction itself. Once the addictive state is established, it functions as a separate morbid state with its own set of dynamics. Treating the social or personal factors shaping toward addiction has no effect on changing the physiological (evoked symptoms on avoidance and relief on exposure) and psychological (obsessive-compulsive neurosis to continue the addiction and narcissrstic neurosis for the continued seeking of pleasure) aspects of addiction."[19] In summary, the pleasure-pain principle is the motivating force behind the unreasonable obsessive-compulsive behavior of pleasure seeking. Therefore, treatment must respond to the biological needs of the person as well as provide alternatives to the obsessive-compulsive behavior of pleasure seeking.

In 1972, Vic Pawlek, then director of a drug treatment center in Phoenix, reported positive results treating heroin and methadone addicts with three grams of Vitamin C and Vitamin B_3 (niacin) a day.[20]

In 1972, Jordan Scher, M.D., with the National Council on Drug Abuse and the Methadone Maintenance Institute in Chicago, began work with Vitamin C in alcoholism. His first study involved alcoholics. He found large doses of Vitamin C were effective in resisting the effects of alcohol withdrawal, reducing hangover symptoms and speeding recovery from the acute and chronic stages of alcoholism. His successful experience was reported in an international meeting on alcholism in Liverpool, England, in 1973.

Dr. Scher next investigated the ability of Vitamin C to relieve the withdrawal symptoms of narcotic addiction. Patients in a state of narcotic withdrawal often experience muscular pains, cramps, cold limps, vasoconstriction, constipation, muscular tension and fatigue. His research team set up a double-blind study with the use of placebos. Their findings were that Vitamin C "seems to have a moderating and tranquilizing influence on behavior and emotional states so that it is of great assistance in the management of patients who are in the process of detoxification."[21] He concluded, "Vitamin C represented a clear addition to the armamentarium of narcotic addiction treatment on a clinical and statistical basis."[22] Similar results were reported by the San Francisco Drug Treatment Program. Using a total of 227 subjects, this program concluded that "megavitamin therapy using sodium ascorbate (a salt of Vitamin C that has a pH similar to the blood and is therefore not as acid as regular Vitamin C), calcium and other mineral supplements was seen as a cost-effective convenient *safe* way to detoxify narcotic addicts, and is also a way to address the poor nutritional habits of our client population.[23]

I vividly recall that those addicts I have worked with in the corrections system have atrocious diets and are addicted to sweets. They would constantly hunger for donuts, sweetened sodas, chocolates and candy. Their diets are very lacking in vitamins, minerals and fiber. In over ten years, I have not worked with one addict, whether juvenile or adult, who has consumed even a marginally nutritious diet.

Vitamin C and Treatment

Since the early 1930's, when Vitamin C (ascorbic acid) was first synthesized, medical research has been carried out on the physiologic effects of this substance. [24-44] The application of Vitamin C to the detoxification of narcotic addicts was made popular by Drs. Alfred Libby and Irwin Stone in California.

The Journal of Orthomolecular Psychiatry published a report from Drs. Libby and Stone in 1977 on the use of large doses of Vitamin C in the successful detoxification of heroin addicts.[45] They reported on 100 cases in which they detoxified heroin addicts. Besides providing large doses of Vitamin C, they provided their patients with high levels of multivitamins and minerals and a predigested protein solution. They based their approach on the theory that addicts are malnourished in general, protein deficient in particular, and virtually deficient in Vitamin C. This condition they called the "Hypoascorbemia-Kwashiokor Syndrome." In Drs. Libby and Stone's research, all patients reported a loss of craving for drugs while taking large doses of Vitamin C, (between 25 and 85 grams per day) during detoxification. Of the first 30 carefully monitored heroin addicts, 30 successfully withdrew from their addiction with no more than minor discomfort. None of the 30 were reported to have relapsed to their former addictive state. Similar results have been reported by other doctors in the United States and two Australian physicians, Drs. Archie Kalokerinos and Glen Dettman.[46]

A Seattle physician, Dr. Janice Keller Phelps, former Medical Director of the King County (Washington) Center for Addiction Services, has successfully utilized this approach in the treatment of heroin and methadone addicts under carefully supervised conditions. Dr. Phelps reported on her studies to an invitational conference on the treatment of criminal offenders in the fall of 1979 in Oakland, California.[47]

The correlation between near deficiency levels of Vitamin C and behaviors common to addicts was determined nearly a dozen years ago. A study completed by the Department of Internal Medicine at the University of Iowa, and partially funded by the U.S. Army Medical Research and Development Command, in 1970, evaluated a broad range of human behavior during controlled Vitamin C deprivation.[48] The study, done with Iowa State Penitentary inmates, showed that decreasing quantities of Vitamin C increased fatigue, lassitude, depression, and reduced energy. This corresponded with the classical "neurotic triad" of the Minnesota Multiphasic Personality Inventory (MMPI) psychological test, namely, hypochondriasis, depression and hysteria. This triad usually indicates a depressed and withdrawn individual who is concerned with his bodily state. These personality changes occur at a stage of Vitamin C depletion well before obvious clinical scurvy is evident. The same study was completed by the researchers on another set of prisoners from the same population under identical conditions with similar results. In view of this study and numerous others [49-53] the use of Vitamin C in the treatment of addicts, along with an improved diet and other supplements, is suggested. However, once the detoxification program is concluded, it is still very necessary that the ex-addict's psychological, economic and social needs be met. It is at this point that conventional treatment approaches might become more effective.

Diet for Substance Abusers

Mark Worden and Gayle Rosellini described a recommended diet for substance abusers at the Fifth National Drug Abuse Conference in Seattle in 1978. Their work with substance abusers at the Douglas County Council on Alcoholism (Oregon) indicated that diet is an "indispensible part of a biosocial framework for treatment."[54]

As counselors, they found it "frequently difficult for the client to believe that his drinking and emotional discomfort may be related to his eating patterns. Before most clients are willing to alter strongly entrenched dietary habits, they must be convinced that the change will be worth the effort. During the initial sessions, it is the counselor's role to explore the possibility that there may be a connection between the client's eating habits and his life problems."

They found that alcohol and drug-misusing clients usually reported the following symptoms:

Depression	Weight problems
Nervousness	Tiredness, weakness
Anxiety	Dizziness, faintness
Craving for sweets	Morning nausea
Craving for alcohol	Blurred vision
Irritability	Transient muscle aches
Rages	Transient joint pain
Feelings of doom	Insomnia, nightmares
Headaches	

They found that these same clients' typical diets consisted of the following:

No breakfast or a high Sugar Breakfast	Heavy consumption of:
	Sugar
Skipped Meals	White flour
	Caffeine
Light eating during day	Salt
	Alcohol
Heavy eating at night	Tobacco
	Junk food
Refined carboyhdrate snacks	Packaged food

In light of this study, it seems clear that dietary counseling become a mandatory part of any substance abuser's rehabilitation program.

Worden and Rosellini developed a "recommended diet for substance abusers."[55] its basic rules are as follows:

1) Eat at least three evenly spaced well-balanced meals per day.
2) Consume adequate protein daily. (Rule of thumb to determine protein needs: desired body weight divided by 2 - grams of protein daily.) Protein may be of animal or vegetable origin.
3) Consume fresh fruits and vegetables daily.
4) Use only whole grains.
5) Include legumes and nuts.
6) Use salt, dried fruit, coffee, tea or tobacco sparingly.
7) Suggested: fruit, vegetable or protein snack between meals or before bedtime.

Common sense suggestions to their clients were:

1) Overweight? Follow basic rules, but limit fat intake and portion size.
2) Balance meals with protein foods, fruits, vegetables and unrefined starches.
3) Observe how you feel. Don't eat anything that later makes you feel bad.

They were also told to completely eliminate the following foods:

Sugar--white, brown, turbinado, raw
Honey molasses
Corn syrup
White flour
White bread
All soft drinks
Ice cream
Canned fruit
Canned vegetables
Processed or prepacked food

Cakes, cookies, pies, pastries, candy, doughnuts
Breakfast cereals, commercially made granola
Fruit-flavored drinks
Flavored yogurt
Coffee
Tea
Alcohol

These are excellent dietary suggestions. They reduce or eliminate most additives described earlier, reduce consumption of refined carbohydrates and provide far more vitamins and minerals. Their experience was that, if substance abusers followed the recommended diet, they would generally quit all substance abuse.

"If one uses nutrition as an adjunct to counseling", pointed out Worden and Rosellini, one should keep in mind that there is no simple, quick, magic nutritional cure for alcoholism, drug abuse and emotional problems. However, there is much evidence to suggest that attention to dietary factors may help the client more adequately deal with problems and render the counseling process more efficient, productive and rewarding. As one client said, 'I used to feel crazy all the time. Now I only feel that way when I cheat on my diet. I know how to control that. It sure makes it a whole lot easier to stay sober."[56]

References

1. Greenland Imposes Rationing. NIAA Information & Feature Service. IFS. No. 67 December 31, 1979.
2. BERRY, Ralph, BOLAND, James, SMART, Charles and KANAK, James. The Economic Costs for Alcohol Abuse and Alcoholism-1975. National Institute on Alcohol Abuse and Alcoholism, Contract No. ADM 281-76-0016, 1977.
3. ibid.
4. ibid.
5. National Clearinghouse for Alcohol Information and the National Institute for Alcohol Abuse and Alcoholism.
6. Poll Say Typical Youth Takes First Drink At Age 10. NIAAA Information & Feature Service, July 11, 1979, p. 3.
7. WILLIAMS, Roger J. Nutrition Against Disease. Pitman Publishing; New York, 1971, p. 173.
8. POULOS, C. Jean, STODDARD, Donald and CARRON, Kay; Alcoholism, Stress and Hypoglycemia. Davis Publishing; Davis, California, 1976.
9. Summary of the 3rd Report on Alcohol and Health. NIAAA Information & Feature Service, IFS, No. 53, November 30, 1978.
10. SMITH, Russell F. A. Five Year Field Trial of Massive Nicotinic Acid Therapy of Alcoholics in Michigan. J Orthomolecular Psychiatry. 3: 327-331, 1974.
11. HOFFER, Abram and WALKER, Morton; Orthomolecular Nutrition. Keats Publishing; New Canaan, Conn., 1978.
12. HOFFER, Abram; The Relation of Crime to Nutrition. Humanist in Canada. 8:2-9, September, 1975, p. 4-5.
13. BRERETON, Lloyd; Subclinical Pellegra Among Penitentary Inmates. Humanist in Canada. 8: 10-11, September, 1975, p. 7.
14. Alcohol: The Starvation Diet. Science News. 115: 152, March 10, 1979
15. Ibid, p. 152.
16. American Dietetic Association, Special Committee of the Diet Therapy Section. Guidelines for Nutrition Care of Alcoholics During Rehabilitation. ADA, 620 N. Michigan Ave., Chicago, Ill., 1971.
17. BRODY, Nathan. Guidelines in Treating the Alcoholic Patient in the General Hospital Orthomolecular Therapy. J Orthomolecular Psychiatry. 6(4): 340, 1977.
18. BEJEROT, Nils; Addiction: An Artifically Induced Drive. Charles C. Thomas; Springfield, Ill., 1972.
19. PHILPOTT, William H., KHALEELUDDIN, Khaja and PHILPOTT, Katherine; The Relationship Between Addictive Drive and Maladaptive Social Behavior. Presentation to the June 15, 1979, National College of Juvenile Justice, Graduate School, University of Nevada, Reno.
20. Do It Now Foundation, Phoenix, Arizona, 1972.
21. SCHER, Jordan, RICE, Harry, SUCK-OO, Kim, DiCAMELLI, Ralph and O'CONNOR, Helen; Massive Vitamin C as an Adjunct in Methadone Maintenance and Detoxification. J Orthomolecular Psychiatry. 5(3): 196, 1976.
22. Ibid, p. 196.
23. FREE, Valentine and Sanders, Pat; The Use of Ascorbic Acid and Mineral Supplements in the Detoxification of Narcotic Addicts. J Orthomolecular Psychiatry. 7(4): 265, 1978.
24. BARELHEIMER, H.; Vitamin C in the Treatment of Diabetes. Die Medizinische Welt. 13: 117-120, 1939.

25. GUPTA, G.C. and GUHA, B. The Effect of Vitamin C and Certain Other Substances on the Growth of Microorganisms. Ann Biochem Experimental Med. 1: 14-26, 1941.
26. HOLMES, H.N. Food Allergies and Vitamin C. Annals of Allergy. 1: 235, 1943.
27. HOLMES, H.M. and ALEXANDER W. Hay Fever and Vitamin C. Science. 96: 497-499, 1942.
28. FERREIRA, D.L. Vitamin C in Leprosy. Publicacoes Medicas. 20: 25-28, 1950.
29. KLASSON, D.H. Ascorbic Acid in the Treatment of Burns. New York State J Med. 2388-2392, October, 1951.
30. FLOCH, H. and SUREAU, P. Vitamin C Therapy in Leprosy. Bulletin de la Societe DE Pathologie Exotique et de Ses Filiales. 45: 443-446, 1952.
31. SIRSI, M. Antimicrobial Action of Vitamin C on M. Tuberculosis and Some Other Pathogenic Organisms. Indian J Med Sci. (Bombay). 6: 252-255, 1952.
32. RITZEL, G. Critical Evaluation of Vitamin C as a Prophylactic and Therapeutic Agent in Colds. Heluetia Medica Acta. 2: 63-68, 1961.
33. MAGNE, R.V. Vitamin C in Treatment of Influenza. El Dia Medico. 35: 1714-1715, 1963.
34. HOFFER, A. and OSMOND, H. Scurvy and Schizophrenia. Diseases of the Nervous System. 24: 273-285, 1963.
35. STONE, I. On the Genetic Etiology of Scurvy. Acta Genetiacae Medicaé et Gemollogoiae. 15: 345-349, 1966.
36. SCHLEGEL et al. The Role of Ascorbic Acid in the Prevention of Bladder Tumor Formation. Transactions of the American Association of Genito-Urinary Surgeons. 61: 85-89, 1969.
37. PAULING, L. Vitamin C and the Common Cold. W.h. Freeman and Co., San Francisco, California, 1970.
38. SHAFFER, C.F. Ascorbic Acid and Atherosclerosis. Am J Clin Nutr. 23: 27-30, 1970.
39. KLENNER, F.R. Observations on the Dose and Administration of Ascorbic Acid when Employed Beyond the Range of a Vitamin in Human Pathology. J Appl Nutr. 23: 3-4, 1971.
40. STONE, I. The Healing Factor. Grosset and Dunlap, New York, 1972.
41. STONE, I. Vitamin C - A New Dimension. Bulletin National Health Fed. 19(3): 22-25, 1973.
42. STACPOOLE, P.W. Role of Vitamin C in Infectious Disease and Allergic Reactions. Medical Hypotheses. 1(2): 43-45, 1975.
43. CATHCART, R. Using Vitamin C to Treat Viral Diseases. Today's Living, 1977.
44. LIBBY, A. and STONE, I. The Hypoascorbemia-Kwashiorkor Approach to Drug Addiction Therapy: A Pilot Study. J Orthom Psych. 6(4): 300-308, 1977.
45. Ibid.
46. KALOKERINOS, A. and DETTMAN, G. The Orthomolecular Treatment of Drug Addiction, A First Australian Report. New Horizons. 5:2, April, 1979. Published by the Committee of the Biological Research Institute, Victoria, New South Wales, Australia.
47. PHELP, J.K. Use of Ascorbate in Addiction Treatment. Conference on Orthomolecular Treatment of Criminal Offenders, Oakland, California, November 2, 1979.
48. KINSMAN, Robert A. and HOOD, James. Some Behavioral Effects of Ascorbic Acid Deficiency. Am J Clin Nutr. 24: 455-464, April, 1971.
49. LIND, J. A Treatise of the Scurvy (1753); edited by C.P. Stewart and D. Guthrie. Reprinted by Edinburgh University Press, 1953.
50. VILTER, R.W., WOOLFORD, R.M. and SPIES, T.D. Severe Scurvy. J Lab Clin Med. 31: 609, 1946.
51. CUTFORTH, R.H. Adult Scurvy. Lancet. 1:454, 1958.

52. FARMER, C.J. Some Aspects of Vitamin C Metabolism. Federation Proc. 3: 179, 1944.
53. BARTLEY, W.H., KREBS, A. and O'BRIEN, J.R.P. Vitamin C Requirement of Human Adults. Med Res Council Special Report, Serial No. 280. H.M. Stationery Office, London, 1953.
54. WORDEN, Mark and ROSELLINI, Gayle; Role of Diet in People Work: Uses of Nutrition in Therapy with Substance Abusers. J Orthomolecular Psychiatry. 7(4): 253, 1978.
55. Ibid, p. 255.
56. Ibid, p. 256.
57. Coffee May Promote Alcohol Craving. Medical Update & Health Digest. 3(6): 4, December, 1979.

Bibliography

BERJEROT, Nils; Addiction: An Artifically Induced Drive. Charles C. Thomas; Springfield, Ill., 1972.

ISRAEL, Yedy and MARDONES, Jorge; A Biological Basis for Alcoholism. John Wiley & Sons; New York, 1971.

LESSER, Michael; Nutrition and Vitamin Therapy (Chapter Ten, Allergies and Addiction) Grove Press; New York, 1980.

NULL, Gary and Steve; Alcohol and Nutrition; Pyramid Publications; New York, 1976.

PAULING, Linus; Vitamin C and the Common Cold and the Flu. W.H. Freeman; San Francisco, 1976.

POULOS, C. Jean, STODDARD, Donald and CARRON, Kay; Alcoholism, Stress, Hypoglycemia. Davis Publishing; Santa Cruz, Calif., 1976.

STONE, Irwin; The Healing Factor; Vitamin C Against Disease. Grossett & Dunlap; New York, 1972.

WATSON, George; Nutrition and Your Mind. Harper & Row; New York, 1972.

WILLIAMS, Roger J. and KALITA, Dwight K. A Physician's Handbook on Orthomolecular Medicine. Pergamon Press; New York, 1977.

WILLIAMS, Roger J. Alcoholism: The Nutritional Approach. University of Texas Press; Austin, Texas, 1959.

WILLIAMS, Roger J. Nutrition Against Disease. Pitman Publishing; New York, 1971.

VI

FOOD ALLERGIES, BEHAVIOR AND CRIMINALITY

"Can Chocolate Turn You Into a Criminal? Some Experts Say So -- "Food Allergies, Malnutrition are Tied to Violent Acts; A Banana Leads to Blows," The article quoted Dr. K.E. Moyer, professor of psychology at Carnegie-Mellon University; "For an allergic person, eating may lead to beating, biting and battle. While a person who is allergic to pollen suffers a stuffy nose, a person allergic to chocolate or bananas may pass out bloody noses." Dr. William Philpott, an Oklahoma psychiatrist, reported in the same article that allergic reactions to foods and pollutants often trigger violent behavior. He described his 12-year-old patient who became so aggressive after eating a banana that he picked up a stick and tried to hit another patient. This same boy started a fight after eating an apple. In another situation, an 18-year-old youth struck Dr. Philpott after ingesting a minute amount of tobacco. Later he told the doctor he had a hallucination and thought the doctor was a devil since he saw horns on the doctor's head!

Dr. Jose Yaryoura-Tobias, a psychiatrist and former research director of the North Nassau Mental Health Center in New York, described the case of a habitual wife-beater. This man had a severe craving for chocolate, cola drinks and coffee. If he did not eat one of these substances he would become violent.

Food Allergies and Behavior

Psychiatrists, allergists and other physicians have been successfully treating patients with behavioral problems by identifying offending foods and chemicals in their environment.

One of the earliest cases was reported by Dr. B.R. Hoobler in 1916 when he identified infants sensitive to proteins.[2] Studies since then have suggested that adverse reactions to foods can be one of the causes of hyperactivity, nervousness, stealing, learning problems, minimal brain dsyfunction, depression, hostility, aggression, periods of confusion, and irritability. [3-20]

Dr. Robert Forman, a sociologist, provides a similar list in *How To Control Your Allergies* of those mental-behavioral symptoms that have been found to be caused in at least some cases by allergy, as indicated by the fact that they had successfully responded to treatment after detecting and managing their allergies.[21] Dr. Forman asks the question "whether some social deviates-people who cannot hold a job, who get into fights and social scrapes regularly and are difficult to live with, and perhaps who are even legal offenders-have allergy as a contributing cause."[22]

In a 1975 article in *Psychology Today,* The Physiology of Violence Allergy and Aggression, Dr. K.E. Moyer, describes an uncontrollable five-year-old boy.[23] This child had aphasia (poor speech development), an abnormal EEG (brain wave test), and a temper out of control. The child was found to be allergic to chocolate, milk and cola. Seven and a half months after eliminating the incriminating foods from the boy's diet, he showed a normal EEG and his behavior had markedly improved. During a one week period the allergic foods were returned to his diet and his EEG was once again abnormal and his behavior had worsened.

Dr. Alan Cott, a New York psychiatrist, has found many foods to be the major cause of children's behavior problems. In a report to the Huxley Institute for Biosocial Research, Dr. Cott stated that, "The first thing I do with a hyperactive child is remove all soft drinks, cake, cookies, candy, ice cream and sugared cereals from his diet. In nearly every instance, the child is markedly calmer within a very short time."[24] Dr. Lendon Smith, a Portland, Oregon, pediatrician, has reported similar results in his book *Improving Your Child's Behavior Chemistry.*[25]

Recent Scientific Studies Confirm The Food Allergy - Behavior Link

Most articles concerning allergy and learning or behavior problems have been anecdotal, meaning they were not scientifically documented. By the late 1970's, a number of studies had been published scientifically attesting to the food allergy-behavior link.

Drs. David S. King and Marshall Mandell reported in 1978 on a double-blind study of 30 adults tested with 12 allergens and 6 placebos.[26] Patients reported significantly more nervous system complaints (cognitive-emotional symptoms) when exposed to the allergens than the placebo solutions (p values ranged from .002 to .004). Patient complaints included depression, inability to concentrate, anger, irritability and headaches.

Dr. John O'Shea completed a double-blind cross-over study of 15 school-aged hyperactive children.[27] In his study, parents were able to differentiate food extracts from placebo solutions by observing their children's behavior. Dr. J.B. Miller reported similar results in another double-blind cross-over study.[28] Again parents were able to accurately perceive when the children were given the offending foods or received the placebos.

Doris J. Rapp, M.D., reports on a double-blind study in the *Journal of Learning Disabilities.*[29] One uncooperative patient, a young man whose mother continued to provide him with the incriminated foods, against Dr. Rapp's advice, had a history of stealing prior to the onset of the study. During the nine months the physician provided either a restricted diet or treated the allergies his stealing stopped. When therapy was discontinued because of the mother's uncooperativeness, stealing resumed. "Within three weeks, five teachers went to the guidance counselor to determine why he was suddenly unable to behave and why he was stealing." Three other patients in Dr. Rapp's study had a recurrence of stealing when therapy was discontinued.

Recently, other researchers suggested that stealing and violence might be food allergy reactions. [30-32] Dr. Richard MacKarness treated a woman in England who had been hospitalized 13 times for violent behavior and depression.[33] She would demonstrate her anxieties by slashing her arm. On one occasion she had thrown her daughter out of her house through a closed window and knocked her three-and-a-half-year-old son unconscious. She was recommended for a lobotomy, a surgical procedure on the brain. At Dr. Mackarness' intervention, she was tested for food reactions and a number of allergic foods were discovered. After being placed on a restricted diet she became content, found employment, and was no longer violent. This case illustrates the possible role of food allergy in some cases of child abuse and neglect. In 1980 it is estimated over one-and-a-half million children will be victims of child abuse or neglect in the United States. One wonders how many children and adults have been drugged and placed in institutions because of violent behavior related to adverse food reactions.

Charles T. McGee, a California physician, has documented numerous cases of children responding adversely to foods and other substances. In his book, *How To Survive Modern Technology,* he describes in detail case after case of children reacting to such substances as corn, cigarette smoke, chlorine, or plastics.[34] Using a number of tests to determine adverse reactions, Dr. McGee has found that most reactions to foods and chemicals are subtle. He has observed reactions occurring at any time, from a few minutes to 72 hours following exposure.

In 1979, I followed Dr. Theron Randolph's treatment of a patient at American International Hospital in Zion, Illinois. She had come to Dr. Randolph because of chronic depression which had not responded to medication or shock therapy. After isolating a number of foods she was reacting to and eliminating them, her condition improved markedly for the first time in years, as evidenced by her energetic and jovial disposition. Dr. Randolph has treated over ten thousand such patients since the 1940's. He was one of the first to relate commonly eaten foods with chronic allergic syndromes often marked by pronounced behavioral changes. [35-38]

In some patients, foods rarely eaten can provoke violently acute reactions. This was first demonstrated clinically in the early 1930's by Dr. H.J. Rinkel.[39] Dr. Rinkel referred to such discoveries as "unmasked food sensitization."

Masked food allergies or food addictions then became related to those foods commonly eaten and producing some adverse reaction when withdrawn.[40] To discover if a person has a masked food addiction, clinical ecologists will subject a person to a three to twelve-day fast. If the person experiences withdrawal reactions, food allergy is suspected. Once the fast is completed, suspected foods are given in separate feedings to discover which food(s) caused the withdrawal symptoms.

Food Allergy and Criminal Behavior

Allergic reactions to foods may be a factor in criminal behavior. Professor Moyer believes food allergies directly affect the body's nervous system by causing a noninflammatory swelling of the brain which can trigger aggression. "The pressure of the swelling may make nerve areas, that normally produce aggression, more sensitive or deactivate areas that normally inhibit aggressive behavior", says Dr. Moyer.[41] He further explains that "the intensity of the symptoms varies from a mild irritable reaction, in which the person is a little more easily annoyed than usual, to the psychotic reaction."

The discovery that allergic reactions can cause violent behavior is considered a recent phenomena, related to our highly processed modern diet. The late Dr. Weston Price, in his classic study, *Nutrition and Physical Degeneration,* notes that allergies are almost never seen in peoples living a primitive lifestyle, eating a natural diet.[42] Dr. Price felt the typical modern diet, high in nonnutritive sugar and refined foods, does not provide optimal nutrition and therefore lowers resistance to allergies. Dr. Carl Pfeiffer, director and chief neuropharmacologist at the Brain Bio Center in Princeton, New Jersey, theorizes that the susceptibility to allergies may be due to a lack of an adequate supply of Vitamin B_6 and zinc in the diet while in utero.[45] Refined carbohydrates, such as white flour and sugar, tend to be practically devoid of either Vitamin B$_6$ or zinc. In 1946, Dr. F.M. Pottenger reported the first case of allergy in a cat in another classic study of the relationship of diet to degenerative disease. Nine hundred cats were divided into four groups and fed different diets. Each group of cats was given the same basic diet. One group of cats was given a diet primarily consisting of raw meat and raw milk. However, cats that were provided with a diet that was two-thirds cooked meat and pasteurized or condensed milk developed many medical problems, including allergies. Cats fed no processed foods and a diet consisting of raw meat, raw milk and cod liver oil remained perfectly healthy. In light of this book's descriptions of the diets of chronic offenders, the food-allergy-criminal behavior theory for some offenders seems plausible.

A Delinquent Suffering From Food Allergy:

One of the sadest cases involving delinquency came across my desk in 1979. A youth with a long history of delinquency and numerous allergies had his prenatal and later medical history described as follows:

"Prenatal history--mother gained 50 pounds and took diuretics to control weight gain...she had high blood pressure during her last two months of pregnancy...toxemia...hospitalized ten days before delivery...the mother very anxious about delivery because her own mother had died in childbirth so labor stopped and had to be induced a month later at 10 months...had to induce six times before delivery occurred...she went into shock (according to mother) and has no memory of delivery...did not see her baby for three or four days...labor had been 72 hours...mother received intravenous glucose for several days after delivery.

"First Three Months---Allergic to all forms of milk...accepted a lamb-based formula...jello water given child since he could not hold down food...had considerable problem breathing regularly... cried constantly...continual runny nose...high temperature and ear infection many times...on several occasions the mother thought he had stopped breathing and would pick him up to get his breathing started again...he was hospitalized several times for severe asthamatic attacks.

"Later History---Lots of tooth decay...hyperactive and hyper aggressive...frequent sore mouth...needs ear cleaned regularly by physician...ear starts to bleed periodically...has bad constipation... find *that he is allergic* to feathers, cats, milk chocolate, beef, pork, ragweed, sage, bermuda, grass and dust...has skin problems... very susceptible to colds.

"School---When reading he skips over words...has short attention span...has a small motor coordination problem that effects his writing...is clumsy.

"Physical Condition as Youth--Suffers many headaches, colds, stomach aches, bone aches, insomnia, swollen neck glands, nervousness, lower back pains, stuffy nose, depression, hot flashes with profuse sweating, canker sores in mouth, hay fever, and early morning and late evening coughing...it frequently takes him several hours to find a position in bed in which he can breath and fall asleep...eyes very sensitive to light.

"Diet---Eats mostly TV dinners in evening...eggs and sausage every day with lots of white bread...lots of milk...lots of canned fruit...no vegetables...gets sick when he eats chocolate, candy, cookies, cake, soda, hot dogs, dates, clams and some cheeses... feels better after he has stopped eating candy for many days."[43]

The probation department that sent this case history was nutritionally oriented. They indicated that, after only three weeks of encouraging the family to make radical improvements in their diet, all of this youth's symptoms were reduced for the first time in his life! One has to wonder why probation officers should be the first professionals to recommend nutritional changes in such a case in the 13 years he had been alive. As Dr. Leonard Hippchen, professor of criminology at Virginia Commonwealth University, has said, "Whereas in the past the role of biological factors in crime largely has been rejected by criminologists, it now appears to be time to work out a new partnership with the nutrition researcher and physician."[44]

Food Allergy Factors

According to Dr. Frederic Speer, a Kansas clinical ecologist, the more common offending foods are:

Cow's milk
Chocolate and cola (the Kula nut family)
Corn (i.e., Cracker Jacks, tortillas, fritos, burritos, bourbon whiskey, many beers, etc.)
Eggs (i.e., mayonnaise, breaded foods, noodles, icing, etc.)
Pea family [chiefly the peanut] (i.e., snap beans, dry peas, etcc.)
Citrus fruits (oranges, lemons, limes, grapefruits, tangerines)
Tomatoes
Wheat and other small grains (i.e., rice, barley, oats, wild rice, millet, rye. etc.)
Cinnamon (i.e., catsup, gum, candy, chili, wieners, etc.)
Artificial food colors (i.e., Hi-C, Tang, Kool-Aid, popsicles, jello, heavy antibiotic syrups, soda, etc.)

Other less common foods include:

pork	fish
beef	coffee
onions	shirmp
garlic	bananas
white potatoes	walnuts and pecans

Any food can cause an adverse reaction. Even foods that are rarely known to cause allergic responses.

According to Dr. Charles T. McGee, M.D., dietary malnutrition is an underlying cause of food allergy, superimposed on a hereditary tendency. Evidence for this theory is that people conquer their allergies through good nutrition. Animals develop allergies when malnourished.

People develop allergies to the foods they consume most frequently. *You are allergic to what you are addicted to.* People crave these foods and frequently turn off symptoms by eating them. Avoiding the incriminating food(s) throws them into withdrawal for three or four days. This is not unlike the heroin addict who experiences withdrawal symptoms--achy joints and muscles, stuffy nose, cramps--when off heroin for three or four days. They frequently get high or feel good after eating suspected food(s). Frequent physical complaints are running nose, post-nasal drip, pale complexion, dark circles under eyes, poor concentration, fatigue, insomnia and headaches.

Now return to the previously described case history and review how many of these symptoms were associated with the youth. In this way you are getting a feel for how a counselor or parent can ask about a client or child's history and determine whether a dietary change is adviseable.

It would seem imperative that the corrections system institute programs to screen chronic juvenile and adult offenders for food allergies and poor nutrition. For large institutions it would be practical and beneficial to establish a clinical ecology wing at either the major state reception/diagnostic center or the state's largest institutions and jails. This type of thorough evaluation and screening has the potential for identifying foods or environmental factors contributing to an inmates' impulsive, often unprovoked, periods of aggression or violence. Certainly, the taxpayer has nothing to lose from such a program. If only 5 percent of the 1979 U.S. inmate population were to benefit from clinical ecology, that would represent over 15,000 prisoners. If a diet-behavior connection is clinically established, an education program can teach the offender how his sensitivity is related to his unruly or antisocial behavior. Then, if the offender continues to consume the "offending" food on the "outside", it will be no one's fault but his own. In the meantime, many offenders remain naive about their possible problems.

References

1. SCHELLHARDT, Timothy D. Can Chocolate Turn You Into A Criminal? Some Experts Say So. Wall Street Journal, front page, June 9, 1977.
2. HOOBLER, B.R. Some Early Symptoms Suggestng Protein Sensitization In Infancy. Am J Diseases Children. 12: 129, 1916.
3. CLARKE, T.W. The Relation of Allergy to Chocolate Problems In Children: A Survey. Psychiatric Quarterly. 24: 21, 1950.
4. DAVISON, H.M. Cerebral Allergy. Southern Med J. 42: 712, 1949.
5. RINKEL, H.J. Food Allergy: The Role of Food Allergy In Internal Medicine. Annals of Allergy. 2: 115, 1944.
6. ROWE, A.H. Food Allergy. Lea and Febiger; Philadelphia, 1931.
7. ROWE, A.H. Allergic Toxicemia and Fatigue. Ann Allergy. 8: 72, 1950.
8. SPEER, Frederick; Allergic Tension-fatigue in Children. Ann Allergy. 12: 168, 1954.
9. WINKLEMAN, N.W. and MOORE, M.T. Allergy and Nervous Diseases. J. Nervous and Mental Diseases. 93: 736, 1941.
10. RANDOLPH, Theron G. Fatigue and Weakness of Allergic Origin (Allergic Toxemia) to be Differentiated from Nervous Fatigue and Neurasthenia. Ann Allergy. 3: 418, 1945.
11. RAPAPORT, H.G. and FLINT, S.H. Is There A Relationship Between Allergy and Learning Disabilities? J School Health. 46, 1976.
12. RAPP, Doris J. Does Diet Affect Hyperactivity? J Learning Disability 11: 383, 1978.
13. KITTLER, F.J. and BALDWIN, D.G. The Role of Allergic Factors In The Child With Minimal Brain Dysfunction. Ann Allergy. 23: 203, 1970.
14. CROOK, William G. Can Your Child Read? Is He Hyperactive? Professional Books; Jackson, Tennessee, 1977.
15. SWANSON, J. Behavioral Responses to Artifical Color. Presented at the 2nd International Food Allergy Symposium, the American College of Allergists, Mexico City, Mexico, 1978.
16. WILLIAM, J.J., CRAM, D.M., TAUSIG, F.T. and WEBSTER, E. Relative Effects of Drugs and Diet on Hyeractive Behaviors: An Experimental Study. Pediatrics. 61: 811, 1978.
17. RINKEL, Herbert J. RANDOLPH, Theron G. and ZELLER, Michael; Food Allergy. Charles C. Thomas; Springfield, Ill., 1951.
18. CROOK, William G. Your Child and Allergy. Professional Books; Jackson, Tennessee, 1973, p. 20.
19. PHILPOTT, William H. Ecologic Medicine Manual (mimeographed). Oklahoma City, 1975, pp. 2-3.
20. COCA, Arthur F. The Pulse Test. ARC Books; New York, 1959, p. 17.
21. FORMAN, Robert; How To Control Your Allergies. Larchmont Books; New York, 1979.
22. Ibid, p. 126.
23. MOYER, K.E. The Physiology of Violence: Allergy and Aggression. Psychology Today. July 1975, pp. 76-79.
24. COTT, Alan; Report to the Huxley Institute for Biosocial Research, Ohio Chapter (newsletter), March, 1977.
25. SMITH, Lendon H. Improving Your Child's Behavior Chemistry; Prentice-Hall, New York, 1976.
26. KING, David S. and MANDELL, Marshall; A Double-blind Study of Allergic Cerebral-Viscero-Somatic Malfunctions Evoked by Provocative Sublingual Challenges with Allergic Extracts: Statistical Confirmation of the Induction of

Psychological (Mental) and Somatic Symptoms by Provocative Testing. Proceedings of the 12th Advanced Seminar in Clinical Ecology, Key Biscayne, Fla., October, 1978. See, also: King, David S. Effects of Sublingual Testing: A Double-blind Study. Proceedings of the 13th Advanced Seminar in Clinical Ecology, San Diego, California, October, 1979.

27. O'SHEA, John; Sublingual Immunotherapy of Hyperactive Children with Food, Chemical and Inhalant Allergens: A Double-blind Study. Proceedings of the 12th Advanced Seminar in Clinical Ecology, Key Biscayne, Fla., October, 1978.

28. MILLER, J.B. A Double-blind Study of Food Extract Injection Therapy: A Preliminary Report. Ann Allergy. 38: 185, 1977.

29. RAPP, Doris J. Food Allergy Treatment For HyperKinesis. J Learning Disabilities. 12(9): 42-50, November, 1979.

30. WACKER, J.A. The Reduction of Crime Through the Prevention and Treatment of Learning Disabilities (author's momograph), Dallas, Texas, 1974.

31. BORCAL, A. and RABKIN, L.Y. A Precursor of Delinquency': The Hyperkinetic Disorder of Childhood. Psychiatric Q. 48: 384, 1974.

32. MOYER, K.E. The Psychology of Aggression. Harper & Row; New York, 1976, pp. 69-73.

33. MacKARNESS, Richard; Eating Dangerously. Harcourt, Brace, Jovanovich; New York, 1976, chapter one.

34. McGEE, Charles T. How To Survive Modern Technology. Ecology Press; Alamo, California, 1979.

35. SCHLOSS, O.M. A Case of Allergy To Common Foods. Am J Diseases Children. 3: 341, 1912.

36. DUKE, W.W. Food Allergy as a Cause of Illness. JAMA. 81: 886, 1923.

37. ROWE, A.H. Food Allergy: Its Manifestation, Diagnosis and Treatment. JAMA. 91: 1623, 1928.

38. ROWE, A.H. Food Allergy: Its Manifestations, Diagnosis and Treatment. Lea & Febiger, 1931.

39. RINKEL, H.J. The Role of Food Allergy in Internal Medicine. Ann Allergy. 2: 115, 1944.

40. DICKEY, Lawrence D. Clinical Ecology. Charles C. Thomas; Springfield, Ill., 1976, p. 48.

41. SCHELLHARDT, ibid.

42. PRICE, Weston; Nutrition and Physical Degeneration. The Price-Pottinger Nutrition Foundation, San Diego, 1945.

43. Personal communication, 1979.

44. SCHELLHARDT, ibid. Dr. Hippchen is the editor of the volume, Ecologic-Biochemical Approaches to Treatment of Delinquents and Criminals, Van Nostrand Reinhold; New York, 1978.

45. According to Dr. Derek Bryce-Smith, University of Reading, England, "It has been shown by studies of rats, that zinc-deficient mothers give birth to offspring who are seemingly normal but who exhibit as they grow up an increased susceptibility to stress, in comparison with the offspring from mothers adequately supplied with zinc during pregnancy." Environmental Trace Elements and Their Role In Disorders of Personality, Intellect, Behavior, and Learning Ability In Children. Proceedings of the 2nd New Zealand Seminar on Trace Elements and Health, January 22-26, 1979.

Bibliography

COCA, Arthur F. Familial Nonregenic Food-allergy. Charles C. Thomas; Springfield, Ill., 1942.

COCA, Arthur F. The Pulse Test: Easy Allergy Detection. Arco Publishing; New 'York, 1956.

DICKEY, Lawrence D. Clinical Ecology; Charles C. Thomas; Springfield, Illinois, 1976.

FEINGOLD, Ben F. Introduction to Clinical Allergy. Charles C. Thomas; 1972.

HIPPCHEN, Leonard J. (ed.) Ecologic-Biochemical Approaches to Treatment of Delinquents and Criminals. Van Nostrand Reinhold; New York, 1978.

FORMAN, Robert; How To Control Your Allergies. Larchmont Books; Jackson, Tenn., 1973.

MacKARNESS, Richard; Eating Dangerously: The Hazards of Hidden Allergies. Harcourt, Brace Jovanovich; New York, 1976.

McGEE, Charles T. How To Survive Modern Technology. Ecology Press; Alamo, Calif., 1979.

MANDELL, Marshall and SCANLON, L.W. Dr. Mandell's 5-Day Allergy Relief System. Thomas Y. Crowell; New York, 1979.

RANDOLPH, Therron G. Human Ecology and Susceptibility to the Chemical Envrionment. Charles C. Thomas; 1962.

RINKEL, Herbert J., RANDOLPH, Therron G. and ZELLER, Michael; Food Allergy. Charles C. Thomas: 1951.

ROBERTS, Sam; Exhaustion: Diagnosis and Treatment, A New Approach to the Treatment of Allergy. Rodale Books; Emmaus, PA., 1967.

ROTH, June; The Food/Depression Connection: Dietary Control of Allergy-based Mood Swings. Contemporary Books; Chicago, 1978.

ROWE, A.H. Elimination Diets and the Patient's Allergies. henry Kimpton; London, 1944.

ROWE, A.H. and ROWE, A.H. Jr. Food Allergy. Charles C. Thomas; Springfield, Illinois, 1972.

VII
NUTRITION, EXERCISE
AND CONVENTIONAL
APPROACHES

Parents Rate Various Treatments

Dr. Bernard Rimland, director of the Institute for Child Behavior Research in San Diego, collected information from 3,300 parents who had children with severe behavior disorders or autism. Approximately 250 questions were asked these parents concerning their child's symptoms, familial disorders, blood types, drugs taken during pregnancy, etc. The third part of the questionnaire asked a variety of questions, primarily treatment factors which were intended to, or have been reported to, affect the child's behavior. The following tables summarize the findings from an analysis of over 2,000 parent responses.[1]

Table 1. indicates the perceived different effects of various kinds of treatment, including the removal of milk, wheat or sugar from the diet, psychotherapy and operant conditioning, Doman-Delacato patterning, etc. Psychotherapy did the poorest. This is not surprising in view of the number of books reporting similar findings. [2-7] Simple removal of milk, wheat or sugar from the diet was reported to be more beneficial than psychotherapy. This should give considerable credence to the assertions of clinical ecologists who have suggested this for over a half century. Operant conditioning is clearly the most often reported successful approach, which is good news since this is one of the major behavior management techniques taught to special education teachers in colleges and universities. The 14 percent made worse by residential school is interesting and needs further interpretation. Table 2. below compares the effectiveness of drugs to vitamins. Mellaril is the best of the drugs, but clearly inferior to the megavitamins in both helpfulness and safety.

It is clear that a nutritional approach was regarded by parents as more effective and safer than drug therapy. Then why is there still so much drug therapy?

TABLE 1.—PARENT RATINGS OF EFFECTS OF MISCELLANEOUS THERAPIES

Therapy	Number of cases	Percent								
		No definite effect	Possibly helped a little	Total	Some improvement	Definitely helped	Total	Made a little worse	Made much worse	Total
Remove milk	190	37	17	54	13	31	44	1	1	2
Remove wheat	113	41	11	52	14	32	46	1	1	2
Remove sugar	132	28	16	44	24	28	52	3	1	4
Psychotherapy	575	37	22	59	19	16	35	4	2	6
Patterning (Doman-Delacato)	183	25	16	41	20	34	54	2	3	5
Day school	1,354	12	14	26	24	45	69	3	2	5
Residential school	346	12	14	26	26	34	60	7	7	14
Operant conditioning	469	6	10	16	24	58	82	1	1	2
"Talking typewriter" (ERE computerized teaching machine)	50	28	18	46	16	38	54	0	0	0

TABLE 2.—COMPARISON OF PARENT RATINGS OF EFFECTIVENESS OF ALL DRUGS, BEST DRUG (MELLARIL) AND VITAMINS

Therapy	Number of cases	Percent								
		No definite effect	Possibly helped a little	Total	Some improvement	Definitely helped	Total	Made a little worse	Made much worse	Total
All drugs (averaged)	2,693	29	18	47	12	13	25	13	16	29
Best drug (Mellaril)	470	24	21	45	17	18	35	11	9	20
High dosage vitamins	191	10	20	30	22	45	67	2	1	3

Exercise Improves Behavior

Several non-treatment effects were also surveyed by Dr. Rimland, including vigerous exercise. Forty-four percent of the parents felt that vigorous exercise was of some or definite help, while only seven percent felt it made their child worse. Again, this is a better rating than drugs. *This suggests a combination of vigorous exercise, removing certain foods from the diet and giving selected vitamins and minerals may be a very effective approach in helping behaviorally disordered children.*

Regular physical exercise:

increases blood volume and increases the number of oxygen carrying red blood cells,

assists body tissues in metabolizing oxygen more efficiently,

restricts deposition of cholestrol,

has a tendency to maintain cholesterol-free arterial walls,

lowers blood pressure,

reduced triglycerides, and

reduces stress.

Aerobics

Few offenders are known to maintain a regular program of exercise. I recommend the aerobic exercises designed by Dr. Kenneth H. Cooper. [8-10] These exercises demand oxygen without producing an intolerable oxygen debt, so that they can be continued for extended periods. One of the best examples of aerobic exercise is jogging, which increases oxygen consumption and endurance. The aerobic concept improves the body's capacity to process oxygen and deliver it to the tissue cells where it can combine with foodstuffs to produce energy. It also improves the body's ability to remove toxins and repair damaged tissue. More important, it improves the amount and flow of blood reaching the brain. The brain is fed more oxygen and glucose thereby improving its capacity.

The Mayo Clinic reported in 1976 that depressed heart patients consistently expressed increased self-esteem after a period of aerobic exercise. Similar results have been published by psychologists working with depressed clients. This effect of exercise is highly desirable when rehabilitating the offender, as most suffer from poor self-esteem.

Several years ago I worked with a female probationer who required constant tranquilization for her chronic anxiety and depression. She began an aerobic exercise program, consisting of vigorous walking, along with an improved diet. The combination of exercise and diet improved her depression. After eight weeks, with the approval of her physician she was slowly taken off the tranquilizers. She no longer needed them. Exercise is an essential co-factor of a dietary program for offender rehabilitation.

Properly followed, exercise offers little risk. Exercise is an inexpensive and uncomplicated powerful tool for an offender's structured rehabilitation program. In view of aerobic exercises' potential to improve self-esteem, correctional programs should incorporate exercise into their rehabilitation modality.

References

1. RIMLAND, Bernard; Comparative Effects of Treatment on Child's Behavior Drugs, Therapies, Schooling, and Several Non-treatment Events). Publication No. 34, Institute for Child Behavior Research, San Diego, California 92116, June, 1977.
2. GROSS, Martin; The Psychological Society. Random House; New York, 1978.
3. TENNOV, D. Psychotherapy: The Hazardous Cure. Abelard-Schuman; New York, 1975.
4. JURJEVICH, R.M. The Hoax of Freudianism. Dorrance; Philadelphia, 1974.
5. RACHMAN, J. The Effects of Psychotherapy. Pergamon; London, 1971.
6. EYSENCK, H.J. The Effects of Psychotherapy. Science House; New York, 1969.
7. PICKNEY, E.R. and C. The Fallacy of Freud and Psychoanalysis; Prentice-Hall; Englewood Cliffs, N.J., 1965.
8. COOPER, Kenneth H. Aerobics. M. Evans and Co.; New York, 1968.
9. COOPER, Kenneth H. The Aerobics Way. M. Evans and Co.; New York, 1977.
10. COOPER, Mildred and Kenneth H. Aerobics for Women. M. Evans and Co.; New York, 1977.

Films & Slides

Body Beautiful (slides w/audible)   Photo Sound International, Inc.
4151 Memorial Drive, #101-E
Decatur, Ga. 30032

VIII

THERE IS MORE TO COLOR AND LIGHT THAN MEETS THE EYE

Malillumination and Behavior

In 1976, Dr. John N. Ott, a photobiologist, alerted the world to a new factor in childhood hyperactivity, malillumination.

During the first five months of 1973, Dr. Ott, then director of the Environmental Health and Light Research Institute, conducted a pilot project in four first grade windowless classrooms of a school in Sarasota, Florida. In two of the rooms, the standard cool-white fluorescent tubes and fixtures with the solid plastic diffusers (covers) remained unchanged. In the other two rooms, the cool-white tubes were replaced with full-spectrum fluorescent tubes that more closely duplicate natural daylight. Lead foil shields were wrapped around each end of the tubes where the cathodes are located. Aluminum "egg crate" diffusers with an additional grounded aluminum screen grid replaced the solid plastic diffusers in these latter rooms.

The behavior of all the students were then filmed for 90 days, to record any behavior changes, using time lapse photography. A dramatic improvement in behavior was demonstrated in hyperactive children [1-3] The first graders settled down and paid more attention to their teachers in the full-spectrum lighted rooms. Additionally, overall classroom performance improved.

"Exploring the Spectrum"[4] is a film by John Ott which records this experiment. Using the technique of time-lapse photograph, hours pass by in seconds. In this way, the viewer has a unique opportunity to watch and record the movements of the classroom children. One particular child in the experimental class had a severe learning disability. He could not read. However, after 90 days under the new full-spectrum fluorescent[5] lights, the child not only stopped

90

being hyperactive but gained a full year in reading. The before and after pictures of this child demonstrate Dr. Ott's results. Similar results have been reported in the Santa Cruz (California) School District.

Studies done in Russia have also borne out Dr. Ott's experiments. Under full-spectrum fluorescent lights they also saw children become less hyperactive, receive better grades and display good physical health.

Light and Nutrition

Light plays a vital role in overall nutrition. Dr. Ott illustrates this by making a comparison with the automobile. Even though the car may be full of high octane fuel, have adequate motor oil and be in good condition, unless the starter works you cannot run the engine and move the car. In much the same way, the body requires light to start our engine. It is a basic biological response.

Dr. Robert Neer, a clinical researcher at the Massachusetts General Hospital in Boston and a professor at Harvard Medical School, was aware that the body's ability to absorb calcium was diminished by a lack of ultraviolet light from the sun. Since some adults avoid going outside, and even avoid milk with added Vitamin D, adult intake of Vitamin D can be near zero. Investigators suspect, but cannot prove, that insufficient calcium in the body is caused by Vitamin D deficiency. Calcium is considered by many nutrition researchers as nature's tranquilizer. Although the mechanism is not understood, adequate stores of calcium tend to keep a person calm. Dr. Neer and other researchers carried out a study on calcium and untraviolet light at the Chelsea Soldiers' Home in Boston. Comparing a group of ten elderly men living under full-spectrum fluorescent with ten living under cool-white fluorescent, it was found that over the winter calcium absorption in the cool-white group fell by 25 percent, while those living under the full-spectrum lights experienced *increased* calcium absorption by an average of 15 percent. The amount of ultraviolet needed to produce the increase in calcium was much below that needed to cause even a trace of sunburn.

Although the role of full-spectrum light and sunlight on diet and nutrition have received little research attention, I feel readers should heed the advice of Dr. H.L. Newbold, a New York psychiatrist, who considers light to be one of the most common nutritional deficiencies.

Ask any former heroin addict how much light they got when they were addicted. Virtually without exception they report nearly complete avoidance of daylight. Outside they wear sunglasses that block any ultraviolet from getting into their eyes.[6] Much like the children in the windowless classes, adults who break the law could benefit from regular daily exposure to natural daylight. If the juvenile or adult attends school or works in an office lighted by standard cool-white or warm-white fluorescent lights, the lights should be changed to a daylight type or the person should increase their exposure to natural daylight. Acme Dunbar Industries, Chicago, has produced fixtures that use daylight fluorescent tubes and an ultraviolet light, fully grounded and lead shielded, that approximates the spectrum of natural sunlight.[7]

Using Color To Reduce Aggression

Evidence suggests that colors affect the body through the endocrine system. [8-10] Specifically, colors are seen by the eye. Through photoreceptors, colors effect the two master endocrine glands--the pineal and pituitary. [11-13]

In 1978, Dr. John Ott demonstrated to me the influence of the color pink on muscle strength. He requested that I bring my arm straight out in front of my body, creating a 90-degree angle with my arm and body. He then attempted to bring my arm to my side. He was unsuccessful. Then he placed a 12-inch by 24-inch piece of pink construction paper about a foot from my eyes. He once again tried to press down my arm. Regardless how hard I tried, he was able to bring my arm down with ease. Looking into the pink color simply reduced my strength. When a blue card or any other color was placed in front of my eyes and the experiment repeated, my strength remained normal.

The 'Pink Room'

As a result of this provocative demonstration, I suggested that corrections officials try to use a 'pink room' (the pink color is 620 nanometers) to curb physically violent inmates or delinquents. The first correctional facility in the United States to utilize such a 'pink room' was the U.S. Naval Correctional Center in Seattle, Washington.[14]

On March 1, 1979, the Center painted one holding cell a particular bright shade of pink, except for the floor, which remained gray. New confinees are placed in such a holding cell until paper work can be processed. Usually this procedure takes approximately fifteen minutes. However, it is the experience of duty intake officers that the most likely outbursts of anger or violence occur when a new inmate is initially confined.

After 156 days of continuous use, the U.S. Naval Correctional Center, reported to the Bureau of Naval Personnel, Law Enforcement and Corrections Division, that "since initiation of this procedure there have been no incidents of erratic or hostile behavior during the initial phase of confinement."

Similar results have been reported by the Santa Clara County Jail, San Jose, California, and the San Bernardino County (California) Probation Department's Kuiper Youth Center.[15]

According to the Santa Clara County Jail Commander, Capt. Mike Miller, after painting the facility's large holding cell, "the calming influence of pink reduced altercations in the cell by 30 to 40 percent."[16] Dr. Humphrey Osmond, a psychiatrist at Bryce Hospital in Tuscaloosa, Alabama, has had schizophrenic patients stare at pink cloth to reduce stress. Dr. Osmond reports that these patients felt much more relaxed. In a randominzed study at the Veteran's Administration Medical Center in Los Angeles (Brentwood), Chief of Management Sciences, Adam Coutts, reports that patients once confined for less than fifteen minutes in the pink holding room are less involved in later altercations than patients placed in a blue room.[17]

This new development in managing behavior is mentioned to stress the underlying principle that not any one factor is a panacea in controlling behavior. Those that claim proponents of diet or light are offering a panacea are just throwing up a smoke screen without foundation. As with artificial light, here is another example of a behavior management approach that is biochemically based. Utilizing a color to curb aggression does not depend on medication or physical force, two ingredients all too common in correctional institutions.

References

1. OTT, John N. Responses of Psychological and Physiological Functions to Envrionmental Light-Part I. J Learning Disability. 1(5): 18-20; and, 1(6): 6-12, June, 1968.
2. OTT, John N. Health and Light. Devin-Adair; New York, 1973.
3. OTT, John N. Influence of Fluorescent Lights on Hyperactive and Learning Disabilities. J Learning Disabilities. August/September, 1976.
4. Exploring the Spectrum (film) is available from International Film Bureau, Chicago.
5. Contact Acme Dunbar for information on proper lighting fixtures. Acme Dunbar Industries, Inc., 1130 West Cornelia, Chicago, Illinois 60657.
6. OTT, John N. The Eyes' Dual Functions, Part I, II, III. Eye, Ear, Nose & Throat Monthly, Spring, Fall and Winter, 1974.
7. See 5.
8. KRIEG, Wendell J.S. The Hypothalamus of the Albino Rat. J Comparative Neurology. 55(1), May, 1932.
9. WURTMAN, Richard J. and AXELROD, Julius. The Pineal Gland. Scientific American. pp. 50-58, July, 1956.
10. SHIPLEY, T. Rod-Cone Duplexity and the Autonomic Action of Light. Vision Research. 4: 155-177, May, 1964.
11. SALTARELLI, C.G. and COPPOLA, C.P. Influence of Visible Light on Organ Weights of Mice. Laboratory Animal Science. 29(3): 319-322, June, 1979.
12. WURTMAN, Richard J. The Effects of Light on the Human Body. Scientific American. 233(1): 68-77, July, 1975.
13. BIRREN, Faber. Human Response to Color and Light. Hospitals. pp. 93-96, July 16, 1979.
14. SCHAUSS, Alexander G. Tranquilizing Effect of Color Reduces Aggression and Potential Violence. J Orthomolecular Psychiatry. 8(4): 218-221, December, 1979.
15. Personal Communication, San Bernardino County Probation Department, Clinical Services, 1979.
16. New Holistic Approach to Corrections Finds Disciples. Corrections Digest, 10(26): 2-4, December 21, 1979.
17. Personal Communication, Adam Coutts, Veteran's Administration Medical Center, Los Angeles (Brentwood), January, 1980.

Films & Slides

Exploring the Spectrum (film)   International Film Bureau
332 S. Michigan Ave.
Chicago, Ill. 60604

The Coming of the Sun (slides w/audible)   Photo Sound International, Inc.
4151 Memorial Drive, #101-E
Decatur, Ga. 30032

IX
CONCLUSION

Diet, Crime and Delinquency has presented a substantial body of evidence that diet, toxic metals, food additives, insufficient nutrients, food allergy, lack of exercise and malillumination can all contribute to criminal behavior. This book represents only a sample of available case histories and research supporting the importance of these factors in dealing with criminal behavior. Criminal behavior is a complox and myriad problem. It seems existing criminal justice system treatment efforts have gone too far in blaming social and psychological events as the cause of crime to the exclusion of biological and environmental factors.

Currently, the criminal justice system is going nowhere. Instead of spending money to seek effective rehabilitation for criminals and prevention of crime, the money is being spent on larger and more secure institutions and jails. Habitual offenders are viewed as hopeless. Each such declaration costs the taxpayer from $7,000 to $25,000 a year. With over 300,000 prisoners in United States correctional Institutions, this is a substantial drain on the American economy. Additionally, each year over one million children are detained for some period of time in juvenile detention centers across the country. It costs from $6 to $35 a day to hold a child in one of these facilities. How much does fresh fruit, whole wheat bread and vegetables cost per child per day? Did even a tenth of one percent of the over 1.4 million individuals on probation or parole in the United States get any nutrition education?

Criminal behavior is not just "in the mind." Biochemical variables do influence behavior. In 1952, Dean James Simmons of the Harvard School of Public Health declared:

> "There is a special need for a fresh approach to the investigation of mental diseases...May it not be possible that today we are spending too much time, energy and money trying to clean up cesspools of the mind, and that we could more profitably try to discover and remove the specific biologic causes of mental diseases?"

The evidence is mounting that a good diet makes a positive difference when working with some offenders. Dr. Roger Williams wrote that "We should not center all our attention on how to treat criminals...we need to prevent crime." Removing junk foods from the delinquent's diet is not only warranted as a preventive measure, it makes good sense. The brain cannot be expected to show good judgment on a diet of junk. This book recommends that in all criminal cases the offender's diet and metabolism be examined before a treatment plan is chosen. This is especially important in juvenile first offenders.

It was Dr. Michael Lesser, a California psychiatrist, who reminded the U.S. Senate Select Committee on Nutrition and Human Needs of the wise words of the great 12th century physician, Moses Maimonides,

"No illness which can be treated by diet should be treated by any other means."

Appendix I

NUTRITION-BEHAVIOR INVENTORY©

Name_____   Age _____

Male___ Female___   Date_____

THERE ARE 52 ITEMS IN THIS QUESTIONNAIRE. THERE ARE ONLY FOUR
CHOICES FOR EACH QUESTION: NEVER, RARELY, OCCASSIONALLY, OR
USUALLY.   PICK THE ANSWER THAT IS CLOSEST TO HOW YOU FEEL OR
ARE IN EACH SITUATION.   THERE ARE NO RIGHT OR WRONG ANSWERS.
IF YOU HAVE ANY QUESTIONS, ASK THE PERSON WHO IS GIVING YOU
THIS QUESTIONNAIRE.

TO SCORE THE QUESTIONNAIRE, ADD UP THE NUMBER OF RESPONSES
CHECKED UNDER "RARELY", "OCCASSIONALLY", OR "USUALLY." DO
NOT ADD UP THE NUMBER OF RESPONSES UNDER "NEVER."

(FOR EXAMPLE, IF 5 RESPONSES WERE CHECKED UNDER THE RARELY
COLUMN, THE TOTAL NUMBER OF RESPONSES FOR RARELY IS 5.)

FILL IN THE NUMBER OF RESPONSES FOR EACH COLUMN BELOW TO
GET A TOTAL SCORE.

RARELY   ____x 1 = ____(a)
OCCASSIONALLY ____x 2 = ____(b)
USUALLY   ____x 3 = ____(c)

(a)_____ + (b)____ + (c)____ = _____ TOTAL SCORE.

NEVER	RARELY	OCCASSIONALLY	USUALLY	
				1. MY VISION GETS BLURRED OR DOUBLE.
				2. MY GUMS BLEED.
				3. AFTER I FALL ASLEEP I WAKE UP AND THEN CAN NOT GET BACK TO SLE
				4. MY MUSCLES FEEL PAINFUL OR SORE.
				5. I GET HEADACHES.
				6. I HAVE ALLERGIES OR ASTHMA.
				7. I GET CRAMPS IN MY LEGS.
				8. I HAVE ITCHING OR CRAWLING SENSATIONS ON MY SKIN.
				9. I SIGH OR YAWN DURING THE DAY.
				10. MY STOMACH OR INTESTINES ARE UPSET.
				11. IF I MISS A MEAL OR IT IS DELAYED, I NOTICE MY HEART BEAT FAST
				12. I GET MAD OR FURIOUS FOR NO APPARENT REASON.
				13. I EASILY GET BRUISES OR BLACK AND BLUE MARKS.
				14. I HAVE NIGHTMARES OR BAD DREAMS.
				15. I GET FAINT, DIZZY, WEAK SPELLS, OR COLD SWEATS.
				16. IT IS HARD FOR ME TO CONCENTRATE.
				17. I AM SLEEPY AFTER I EAT.
				18. I NIBBLE BETWEEN MEALS WHEN I AM HUNGRY.
				19. I GET JITTERY OR NERVOUS WHEN I AM HUNGRY.
				20. I GET VERY TIRED OR EXHAUSTED.
				21. I NO LONGER FEEL TIRED AFTER I EAT.
				22. I GET HUNGRY OR FEEL FAINT IF I DO NOT EAT OFTEN.
				23. I FEEL BETTER AFTER MY FIRST SNACK OR MEAL OF THE DAY.
				24. I DRINK COFFEE OR TEA IN THE MORNING TO GET STARTED.
				25. I OFTEN FORGET THINGS.

NEVER	RARELY	OCCASSIONALLY	USUALLY	
				26. I EAT SWEET THINGS OR DRINK CAFFEINATED COFFEE, TEA OR COLA.
				27. I HAVE MORE THAN 3 CUPS OF COFFEE, TEA OR COLA A DAY.
				28. I ADD SUGAR TO MOST THINGS I EAT OR DRINK.
				29. I AM VERY RESTLESS.
				30. I FEEL VERY SLEEPY DURING THE DAY.
				31. I DRINK ALCOHOLIC BEVERAGES.
				32. I CAN NOT WORK UNDER PRESSURE.
				33. IT IS HARD TO DECIDE ON THINGS.
				34. I CRAVE SWEET FOODS, CANDIES OR DRINKS.
				35. I FEEL DEPRESSED.
				36. I CONSTANTLY WORRY ABOUT THINGS.
				37. I GET CONFUSED.
				38. I HAVE TROUBLE MAKING DECISIONS.
				39. AT TIMES I FEEL LIKE I AM HAVING A NERVOUS BREAKDOWN.
				40. I GET DEPRESSED OR FEEL THE BLUES OVER NOTHING.
				41. I GET IRRITATED.
				42. I GET IMPATIENT.
				43. I BLOW LITTLE THINGS OUT OF PROPORTION AND EASILY LOSE MY TEMPER.
				44. I GET FEARFUL.
				45. I FEEL VERY NERVOUS.
				46. I EAT WHEN I AM NERVOUS.
				47. I AM HIGHLY EMOTIONAL.
				48. I WANT TO KILL MYSELF.
				49. I CRY FOR NO APPARENT REASON.
				50. I GET DROWSY.
Totals				

51. WHAT TWO FOODS DO YOU LIKE OR CRAVE THE MOST?
A._____ B._____

52. DO YOU SMOKE CIGARETTES? YES____ NO_____

Appendix II

DIETS OF JUVENILE OFFENDERS.

TABLE 1

NUTRITIONAL DATA

Vitamins

	RDA	Controls N=22(Males) Ave.	Delinquents N=22(Males) Ave.
Vitamin A (I.U.)	5000	35.742	8,577
Vitamin A (R.E.)	1000	2,156	2,425
Vitamin E (I.U.)	12	15.4	18.0
Vitamin D (I.U.)	400	443	861
Vitamin K (mcg)	Not est.	404	509
Thiamin/B_1 (mg)	1.4	1.8	2.54
Riboflavin/B_2 (mg)	1.7	3.2	5.14
Niacin/B_3 (mg)	18.2	28.7	35.7
Pyridoxine/B_6 (mg)	1.6	2.5	3.2
Pantothenic Acid (mg)	5-10	13.4	20
PABA (mg)	Not est.	16.6	27.3
Folic Acid (mcg)	400	214	252
Vitamin B_{12} (mcg)	3.0	9.3	10.4
Biotin (mcg)	Not est	93.4	128
Choline (mg)	Not est.	653	825
Inositol (mg)	Not est.	714	805
Pangamic Acid (mg)	Not est.	13.8	22
Vitamin C (mg)	45	152	203
Bioflavonoids (mg)	Not est.	16.8	12.6

Minerals

	RDA	Ave.	Ave.
Calcium (mg)	1200	2380	2916
Magnesium (mg)	350	388	588
Phosphorous (mg)	1200	2286	3506
Sodium (g)	Not est.	4.9	5.3
Potassium (g)	2.5	4.5	6
Iron (mg)	18	20	22.7
Copper (mg)	2-5	2.5	3
Manganese (mg)	2.5-5	2.8	3.5
Zinc (mg)	15	19.7	34
Chromium (mcg)	50-200	220	227
Selenium (mcg)	50-200	128	185
Iodine (mcg)	130	224	252
Nickel (mcg)	Not est.	279	320
Molybdenum (mcg)	Not est.	143	178
Vanadium (mcg)	Not est.	63	47

Significant Ratios:

	RDA	Ave.	Ave.
Calcium: Phosphorous	1.0	1.0	.83
Calcium: Magnesium	2.3-4.0	6.13	4.96
Sodium: Potassium	1.0-3.0	1.1	.88
Zinc: Copper	7.5	7.85	11.21

Acid Alkaline

		Ave.	Ave.
Acid Ash		52%	49%
Alkaline Ash		48%	51%

Essential Amino Acids

	RDA	Ave.	Ave.
Tryptophan	245	1492	2246
Phenylalanine	1350	5563	8483
Leucine	2577	10068	15236
Isoleucine	1718	6458	9683
Lysine	2700	8712	12905
Valine	1534	6827	10380
Methionine	1350	2828	4058
Threonine	1718	5257	7973

Fats

Cholesterol	Not est.	644	840
Saturated Fatty Acids	Not est.	106	97
-Linoleic Acid (Vit K)	3-6	15	19
-Oleic Acid	Not est.	51	70
Unsaturated Fatty Acids	Not est.	66	89

Food Analysis

	RDA	Ave.	Ave.
Calories/Kcal.		3,426	4,703
Carbohydrates/g		376	507
-refined/%		65.5	62.1
-unrefined/%		34.6	37.9
Protein/g		128	183
Fat/g		165	217
-% calories from fat		43	42
Dietary Fibert/g		19.7	23.5

Food Guide

(Daily Servings)			
Dairy Products		4.3	7.9
Protein Foods:			
-animal sources		2.7	3.2
-legumes, nuts		.33	.57
Fruits and Vegetables:			
-Vitamin C-rich		.73	.68
-dark green		.27	.25
-other		2.23	2.11
Whole Grain Products		.68	.99
Fats and Oils		1.23	1.41
SUGAR (tsp.)		28.7	38
(hidden in food and beverages)			

Index

OTHER TITLES AVAILABLE FROM PARKER HOUSE

"NUTRITION AND VITAMIN THERAPY"
BY MICHAEL LESSER, M.D.

Trained at two of this country's finest medical institutions, Cornell Medical College and Albert Einstein Medical Center, Dr. Lesser, Founding President of the Orthomolecular Medical Society, presents the first plain-talking guide to the use of nutrition and vitamin therapy. Illustrated with actual case histories, he explains how vitamins, minerals, toxic metals, food allergies, blood sugar and diet affects the health, well being and sexual vitality of all of us. Includes tables of usage, illustrations, graphs, references and index. Grove Press Quality Paperback 240 p.

"NUTRITION AND MENTAL HEALTH"

Includes the complete HEARING Before The SELECT COMMITTEE ON NUTRITION AND HUMAN NEEDS Of The UNITED STATES SENATE, PLUS, the original papers of the Foremost Scientists and Physicians in the field; LINUS PAULING, ABRAM HOFFER, ALAN COTT, CARL C. PFEIFFER, EMMANUEL CHERASKIN, BEN FEINGOLD, MICHAEL LESSER, HARVEY ROSS, THERON RANDOLPH, IRWIN STONE and many others. This valuable reference is the most comprehensive coverage of this subject available in a single volume. Fascinating reading for everyone, an indispensable tool for the professional. Parker House Quality Paperback 340 p.

ORDER FORM IS ON THE NEXT PAGE

Order Form

Please send to; (Name) _____

(Address) _____
(City, State) _____
(& Zip Code) _____

_____ copy(ies) of "NUTRITION And VITAMIN THERAPY" @ $9.95

_____ copy(ies) of "NUTRITION And MENTAL HEALTH" @ $6.95

_____ copy(ies) of "DIET, CRIME And DELINQUENCY" @ $6.95

Orders of $15.00 or less, please enclose $2.00 for postage and
handling. Orders over $15.00 are postage paid

California residents please enclose 6½% sales tax

Canada and Foreign Countries please remit   Total $ _____
payment in U. S. Dollars only.

Please make check payable to Parker House, and enclose with your order from;

PARKER HOUSE, 2340 PARKER STREET, BERKELEY, CALIFORNIA, 94704

(415) 845-0700